MY WARD

The story of St Thomas', Guy's and the Evelina Children's Hospitals

and their ward names

Wendy Mathews

Published in 2009 by Walpole House Publishing
London, England
Reprinted with corrections 2011

Copyright © 2009 Wendy Mathews

A CIP catalogue record for this book is available from the British Library

ISBN 978-0-9563942-0-0

Designed by Axiom Design Partnership Limited
axiom@madasafish.com

Printed and bound in Great Britain by
Quentin Press Limited
Victoria Road, Burgess Hill, West Sussex
RH15 9LR

Further copies of this book are available from: mathews.myward@gmail.com

"… 'tis man's worst deed to let things that have been run waste,
and in the unmeaning present sink the past…"

From the sonnet to John Lamb Esq.
Works of Charles and Mary Lamb IV 1805 – 1820

PICTURE CREDITS

FOREWORD
Wendy Mathews © Tony Walsby

ST THOMAS' HISTORY AND WARDS
Florence Nightingale photographs
© The Florence Nightingale Museum

St Thomas' Chapel © Alan Bird

Evelina overlooking the Thames
© Paul Tyagi for Hopkins Architects Ltd

Jacob Wrestling with the Angel
© Gloumouth1

The hospital at Scutari
© The Florence Nightingale Museum

GUY'S HOSPITAL AND WARDS
Thomas Guy discussing the plans for his
hospital Painting by C W Cope, R.A. 1877
© Guy's and St Thomas' Charity

Statue of Thomas Guy © Alan Bird

A Day at Guy's Hospital by G Earle Wickham
© Guy's and St Thomas' Charity

Guy's Mini Museum © Alan Bird

Keats statue in the Old London Bridge Alcove
© Piers Allardyce for Guy's and St Thomas'
Charity

Madonna and Child by Jason Brooks
© Guy's and St Thomas' Charity

EVELINA HISTORY AND WARDS
Photographs of Charlotte de Rothschild,
Baroness Evelina de Rothschild, Ferdinand
Rothschild, watercolour of The Elector of Hesse
entrusting Mayer Amschel with his treasure,
by J Oppenheimer all reproduced with the
permission of The Rothschild Archive.

Photographs of 'The Tree of Life' by Chris
Plowman and 'Children of the World' by
Frederick Landowsky © Richard Bailey

CONTENTS

Foreword 8

Acknowledgements 10

Introduction 12

Chapters:

St Thomas' Hospital
History 14
Wards 44

Guy's Hospital
History 72
Wards 88

Evelina Children's Hospital
History 108
Wards 118

Derivations of other names 124

Sources 130

Alphabetical lists:
Wards by Hospital 133
Other names 135

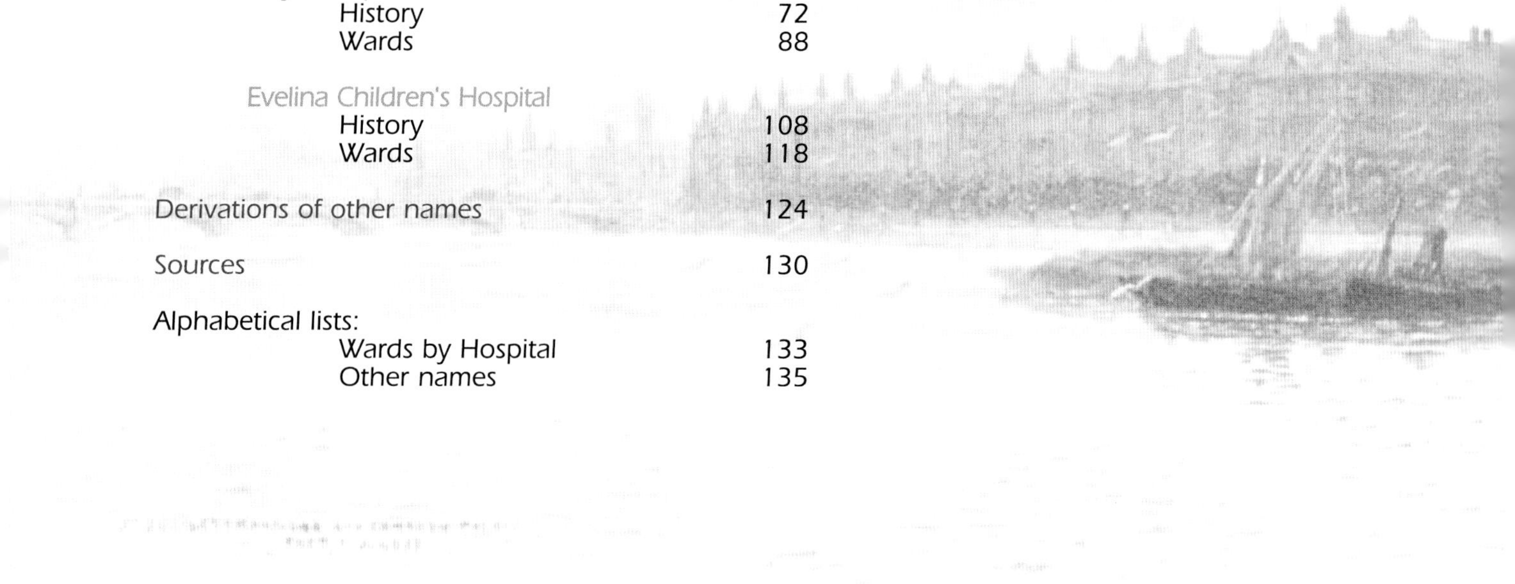

FOREWORD

The Guy's and St Thomas' NHS Foundation Trust has comprised St Thomas', Guy's and the Evelina Children's Hospital since 2004. Much has been written of the Hospitals' histories but, to the best of my knowledge, there is no other reference book detailing the origins of the ward names. Yet, over the centuries, the names of the wards give a fascinating insight into general and medical history and the preoccupations and changing values of the Hospitals and their times.

This work details the history of the ward names of the Hospitals over the centuries, providing some insight into why these names were chosen. Wards and other listed names are printed in bold type.

When I entered the Physiotherapy Training School in 1954, I could not foresee that St Thomas' would always be an important element in my life. After qualifying and 10 years of marriage, my husband John began to share my interest in St Thomas'. His clinical training had been at Guy's, but he became Senior Registrar and subsequently Consultant in Rheumatology at St Thomas'. Rheumatologists and physiotherapists were in adjacent departments and, from 1978 – 1984, I worked in the Physiotherapy Department on research projects directed by my husband. From 1983 until the present day I have been involved with plans for, and in volunteer support of, the Florence Nightingale Museum (FNM).

From the outset of my association with St Thomas' I was interested in its ward names. Early in their training the physiotherapy students undertook one month of ward nursing duties. The current Sister Charity was not over-charitable when it came to my poor ability at bed-making but thanks to her my enduring loyalty to the Florence Nightingale tradition began. I became a life-long member of the St Thomas' family and as tour guide and lecturer for the FNM and the Hospital enjoy enthusing others about its history and legacy.

With the advent of the Guy's and St Thomas' NHS Trust (subsequently Foundation Trust), my loyalty has, of necessity, expanded to cover three Hospitals. The scope of this book therefore encompasses the original ward names and the developments which led to changes in those names at St Thomas', Guy's and the Evelina Children's Hospitals. Smaller hospitals have been subsumed over the years. Where ward names have been adopted by the parent hospital, I have sought their origins too.

Over the centuries there has been dispute concerning the spelling of St Thomas'. St Thomas and St Thomas's are variations which have been used but which have now been dropped in favour of St Thomas' which is therefore used throughout this book.

I have referred extensively to past works on the histories of the Hospitals and am grateful to those who undertook research into primary sources. Without their efforts, this book, and the fully referenced concise history which is lodged at the London Metropolitan Archives, would not have been produced.

I hope this book provides as much pleasure and interest to others as its compilation has given to me.

Wendy Mathews
London October 2009

Photograph © Tony Walsby

ACKNOWLEDGEMENTS

In the late 1980s I studied with the Open University (OU), obtaining my degree in 1989.

The importance of seeking primary sources of information and making legible notes were fundamental elements of the three-month preparatory course. Over the following four years I learned the pleasure of library-based research. These aspects of study have proved invaluable as I collected data for My Ward. So my first thanks go to the OU tutors in the Arts and Social Sciences Faculties.

Early in 2006, Mr Donald G Bompas JMN CMG (erstwhile Secretary to Guy's Hospital Medical School and then to the United Medical and Dental Schools of Guy's and St Thomas') sent me a list of references to Guy's ward names. He also sent me information from the late Audrey Crump, who was Director of Nursing at the time of the closure of the Evelina and its move to Guy's Tower. I am indebted to them both.
I am grateful to numerous other individuals for their personal communications which formed the essential stepping stones of my research. Whether I asked for information on a ward or questioned a retired friend, I was received with interest and enthusiasm by Irene Bonnici, Lisa Burnapp, Laura Byers, Stewart Cameron, Sandra Carnall, Gordon Cook, Daphne Fallows, Helen Fawcett, John Ford, Danielle Harari, Fred Heatley, Joyce Hemming, Mia Hilborn, Joanna and Kevin Hoffman, Norman Jones, Michael Joseph, Ann Keane, Bernd Koschland, Mary Lansdell, Clara Lowy, Mary Magowan, Edward Mansell, Darryl Maxwell, Mike Messer, Gill Moore, Hugh Murray, Michael O'Brien, Ann Packer, Penny Pickering, Judith Pottinger, Tony Rudd, Alison (Tarratt) Ruoff, Gloria Sankey, Karen Sarkissian, Richard Sawyer, Geoffrey Spencer, Doreen Stebbings, Colin Stern, Liz Stratton, Chris Thomas, Sir Richard Thompson, Natalie Tiddy, Pauline Ward, Janet Watters, Delores, Francine, Harriet, Jo, Katie, Marion, Tina and many more.

Librarians have been generous with their time. My thanks to the staff of King's College London who manage the medical school libraries and archives, to Bridget Howlett of the London Metropolitan Archives and Barbra Ruperto of the Rothschild Archive, to Peter Basham, Julie Beckwith and Luca Dussin of the Royal College of Physicians Heritage Centre, to Stephen Humphrey and Stephen Potter of Southwark Local History Library, to Fiona Bourne and Frances Woodrow of the Royal College of Nursing Archives in Edinburgh, to James Armstrong of the Worshipful Company of Stationers and Newspaper Makers, to Philip Bye at the East Sussex Records Office, Sarah Millard and Lara Webb at the Bank of England Archive, to the staff of the British Orthopaedic Association, the Journal of Bone and Joint Surgery, the Maughan Library, the Royal College of Obstetricians and Gynaecologists, the Royal College of Midwives and the Royal College of Surgeons of England.

I am grateful for the unfailing interest and support of Guy's and St Thomas' NHS Foundation Trust and King's College London, in particular Karen Sorensen of Capital and Estates, Ann Carey of the Evelina Children's Hospital and Bill Edwards of the Gordon Museum. It was helpful to have access to the libraries of the Florence Nightingale Museum and the Nightingale Fellowship.

Without Carol Harris, editor, and Elaine McLaren, designer, this book could not have been produced and, of course, my thanks to the Guy's and St Thomas' Charity for the funding which has made the project possible.

But above all others for his many helpful comments and tolerance over the past three years to my husband John "Thank you".

INTRODUCTION

From their inception monasteries and convents were institutions for prayer, meditation and welfare. All had an infirmary (Latin infirmus – not strong) for their own sick and the local sick poor. Unfortunately the records of St Mary Overie, which opened in 1106 as St Mary the Virgin and became the St Thomas' Hospital of this book, were burned in 1212. However there are records that in 1123 poor patients were admitted into the infirmary of St Bartholomew's in the City of London. Infirmaries became known as spitals (spit places) where those with suppurating and spit producing conditions (named the foul diseases) were cared for. The use of the word Hospital (from the Latin hospitis – guest) began during the 17th century.

Why do hospitals have "wards"? In the middle ages, rooms in which groups of people slept would have been known as dormitories (Latin - dormitorium, from dormire - to sleep). However, the sick needed much more than sleep. All who are ill require care, protection and watching over. "Ward" covers all these requirements.

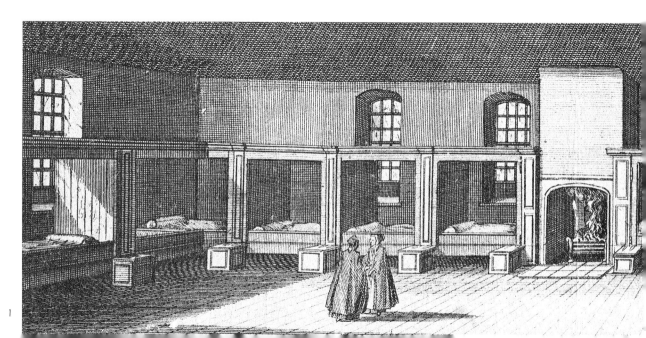

1

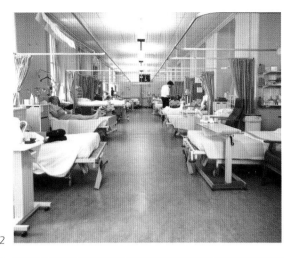

According to Chambers Dictionary (2003), "ward" is derived from the old English word "weardian" and the old German word "warten" meaning to wait, attend or take care of.

To name the hospital rooms into which those sick in body or mind are admitted for care and, whenever possible, cure, "ward" was and is an obvious choice.

2

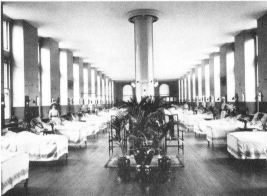

3

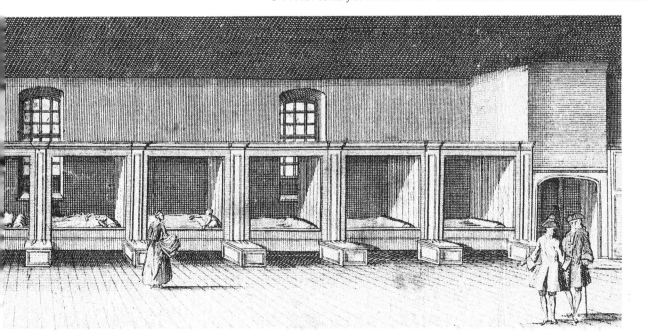

1 An 18th century ward from an engraving, *Guy's Hospital for Incurables, 1725*, by Thomas Bowles
2 A typical 20th century ward
3 A 19th century St Thomas' ward

ST THOMAS' HOSPITAL

ORIGINS 1100 – 1600

The early history of St Thomas' Hospital is uncertain as, in 1212, a disastrous fire destroyed all its records. However, it is recorded elsewhere that in 1100 the church of St Mary the Virgin stood in the yard of Southwark Cathedral, which was in the Diocese of Winchester. The church became known as St Mary Overie, probably because it was "over" the River Thames from the City of London.

In 1105 Henry I welcomed the Order of Austin (Augustinian) Canons to England. The Bishop of the Diocese, William Gifford, saw the Canons' concern for the welfare of the poor and persuaded the secular clergy of Southwark to become members of the Order. In return he built them a priory. This 1106 building had an infirmary in the church (probably adjacent to the Lady Chapel) which would originally have been for sick clergy. However, it is almost certain that the Canons and Canonesses shared all they had with their

neighbours and tended the sick poor.

In 1173, three years after the murder of Archbishop Thomas Becket, the infirmary of St Mary Overie was renamed St Thomas' Spital in tribute to the newly-canonised priest.

Following the fire in 1212 when the priory was totally destroyed, Pierre des Roches, Bishop of Winchester, arranged for the rebuilding of the priory on its original site. He donated Diocesan land to the east for a new spital and chapel, to be administered by a secular Master. Gradually successive Masters achieved independence from the Prior.

Over the next 300 years benefactors, possibly hoping to gain eternal salvation, were generous and the Spital prospered. Donations

2

3

of money, property and land in London and beyond were made but available funds were always insufficient to meet needs, despite the efforts of the Masters. St Thomas' could accommodate 40 patients and was never short of applicants. They came from the local citizens who were poor, ill-fed and often sick due to the unhealthy marshland that surrounded them. They also came from travellers making the pilgrimage to Canterbury. As the chapel, refectory and kitchens occupied most of the ground floor space, it is assumed that patients were taken up the outside staircase to a second storey - the solar - referred to as **Noah's Ark**.

The beds were piles of straw on the floor and it is unlikely that there were any partitions.

In 1507, the infirmary was rebuilt using plaster

and thatch which stood, with some brick- built additions, for nearly 200 years. St Thomas' was closed for 12 years when Henry VIII seized the assets of monasteries and convents but in 1553 his son, Edward VI, as Founder and Patron, approved its 1552 reopening, with the "Royal Hospitals' Charter". The Hospital was dedicated to Thomas the Apostle. Later it was also rededicated to St Thomas Becket, hence "St Thomas's" Hospital. The Hospital was generously endowed with City of London property and, until the advent of the NHS, was administered by the 30-strong Grand Committee of the Court of Governors, drawn from liverymen of the City of London.

4

Ward names were probably in use from the 1550s but **King's**, **Queen's** and **Sweat** were not recorded as being in use until 1562, and **Luke** was only first recorded in 1565.

1 St Mary's Priory, Southwark

2 St Thomas Becket

3 The new hospital, 1507

4 Henry VIII

5 Edward VI

5

Twenty-five nursing sisters cared for between 100 and 250 patients who were all "Presented" to the Master for discharge. "P" was written on their notes, a practice which continued until the mid 20th century.

By 1576, 10 wards had been recorded: the **Sweat wards** - **Job**, **Judith**, **Lazarus** and **Susanna** and the **Great Wards** - **King's**, **Queen's**, **Jonas**, **Magdalen**, **Nightlayers** and **Noah's Ark**. At the same time **Lydia** appears for the first time and it is recorded that, in 1583, **Abraham**, **Isaac** and **Jacob** were built.

FOUNDATIONS FOR A MODERN HOSPITAL 1600 – 1700

Over the next 100 years the Governors' Reports note only four new ward names. In 1602 over-night lodgers were no longer admitted and **Nightlayers** was renamed **Tobias**. Nearly 40 years later, during Cromwell's Puritan rule, **Abdiel**, **Dorcas** and **Faith** were opened. There were other developments. The Governors formed small committees to oversee the day-to-day running of the Hospital. Patients included the war wounded, victims of the plague and the Great Fire of London as well as citizens from the local slums or those plucked from the swirling River Thames.

The medical staff inaugurated the practice of having assistants known as "skillet (long handled pan) carriers", later known as pupils and later still, medical students. Physicians, both masters and pupils, were educated, often wealthy and mainly well-disciplined.

Surgeons were generally skilled but not necessarily well-educated and were, on occasions, dismissed for inappropriate behaviour such as brawling. The moral character of some sisters was also a problem. Drunkenness was the most common reason for disciplinary action. Water was often polluted so small (weak) beer and gin were drunk instead.

The sisters slept on their designated wards whether male or female leading to promiscuity. Improper use of funds was rife. Only

with the advent of the Nightingale Training School for Nurses in June 1860 was professional discipline introduced into nursing.

The 1666 Great Fire of London did not cross the river but, in 1676, fire again broke out in Southwark. Thomas Hollyer, Hospital Clerk, lived adjacent to **Jonas**. His house was blown up to save the Hospital but only after his servant, Richard Finch, had rescued all the Hospital's records. Finch's reward was 40 shillings.

Five years later the Governors decided to build a gateway facing Southwark High Street. The old entrance was too narrow "awry … and very obscure but the new one will be quite obvious and may attract contributions". The frontispiece of Purbeck stone was inset with a statue of Edward VI, his Coat of Arms and four small figures known as "the cripples". Today the stone statue of Edward VI stands at St Thomas' main entrance and the four figures are exhibited on the first floor.

Until 1690 the monarch influenced appoint-ments to the Court of Governors but that year the "good sense" of William III prevailed and royal favourites were no longer guaranteed seats on the Board. Sir Robert Clayton was soon appointed and later gave exceptional service as President.

By the late 17th century St Thomas' required refurbishing. In 1686, the Governors had discussed the poor sanitary conditions. The water supply needed improving. There were numerous sources of "unpleasant smells" and the fire hazard was omnipresent. Conditions were made worse when some windows were bricked up after the window tax was introduced in 1696. Treatments had altered, requiring additional space, not least because patients now had a bed each! A new brick-built hospital would redress all these issues. The rebuilding fund appeal was launched in 1693. When it closed in 1720, £37,769 had been raised.

REBUILDING AND FAREWELL
1700 – 1862

Building started as funds became available and the project was mainly completed by 1709. St Thomas' stood, with some additions and alterations, until compulsorily demolished in 1862. The new Hospital consisted of three large colonnaded courts and a small court at the rear of the third (east) court. The buildings were classical in style with staircases set in the corners.

The Governors ordered that all wards should have a name plate above the entrance door, a practice which continues today.

The first court was named Clayton Square, after Sir Robert, and was completed by 1701. It was built on the site of the original Spital although the rectangular plot now extended to Southwark (Borough) High Street to the west. The new buildings housed the men's wards **Isaac** (16 beds), **Jacob** (29 beds), **Job** (25 beds), **Jonah** (26 beds), **King's** (30 beds),

Abraham (15 beds), **Tobias** (19 beds) and **Noah** (21 beds). Beyond the Square were two salivating wards **Lazarus** (16 beds) and **Susannah** (17 beds). Patients with ague (burning fever) and malaria (hot and cold fits) were at this time widely treated with herbals such as a "diet drink", possibly guiacum or scurvy grass, to stimulate saliva production. Mercury was also administered, in ever-increasing doses, until the unfortunate patient produced frothing saliva. Adjacent were the seven-bedded **Cutts** ward for lithotomy (surgery to remove stones), a bath-house and the dead house (mortuary). To the rear of these was the cemetery. Three years later, **Lazarus** was converted to house the fire engine and **Susannah** became a foul ward (for patients with syphilis).

By 1704 the central court was under construction. The buildings included St Thomas's Church which was open for public worship and the Treasurer's House, both of which stand today. The patients' chapel was also part of this administrative court. Thirty years later, following the erection of his statue, this court was renamed Edward Square.

The Fore Court, at the west of the development was built between 1707 and 1709 with wards for female patients on three levels. On the north side were **Elizabeth**, **Mary** and **Anne**. On the south side were **Lydia**, **Queen** and **Dorcas**. The benefactors whose gifts enabled the building of these wards were both Governors. They were Thomas Guy who, within the next 15 years, was to fund the building of his own hospital, and Thomas Frederick.

With over 200 beds in new buildings, St Thomas' was respected and famous. The three staff physicians and three staff surgeons were developing a medical school. The appointment of two great medical men, Richard Mead, physician, and William Cheselden, surgeon, who joined the staff in 1703 and 1718 respectively, had a considerable impact on the success of the school.

Mead was an adept physician and, later, was a Governor of both St Thomas' and Guy's Hospitals.

Cheselden was renowned for wearing a silk turban rather than the customary powdered wig.

What is not so well known is that in 1727, Cheselden designed the first Putney Bridge which, one year later, spanned the River Thames between Fulham and Putney. The craftsman for Putney

1 Richard Mead
2 William Cheselden

Bridge was Thomas Phillips, who made wooden legs for Cheselden's amputees and was also carpenter to King George II.

In 1708 **Abraham** was converted into a store and cellar. In 1717 new foul wards were built in the backyard to the east of Clayton Square. Two were named **Job** and **Magdalen**, the third **Naple's** (or **Naples**). In 1730 **Naple's** and **Magdalen** were designated as foul fluxing wards. **Job** and **Susannah** were the clean fluxing wards. Patients with gastro-intestinal problems resulting in diarrhoea were said to have "the flux" and foul fluxing wards were probably for syphilitic patients.

During the 18th century there were some ward name changes. These reflected the Governors' desire to compliment royalty rather than to imbue patients, staff and potential donors with biblical symbolism. Three male wards were renamed **Edward** (1734), **William** (1735) and **George** (1741). **Luke** reappeared but **Jonah**, **Noah** and **Tobias** were no longer used. The Governors' Reports of July 1782 note that **Susannah** was renamed **Henry**. Social changes were also reflected in changes to the Hospital. Window tax was again avoided by "bricking-up". In the 1750s all sisters were called nurses, possibly an anti-Catholic reaction. A library, museum and lecture hall were built to facilitate new training methods. In his 1819 account of the Hospital, Benjamin Golding describes St Thomas' as "a neoclassical gem". Ideally proportioned and spacious, it was perfectly designed for its purpose with 19 wards and 453 patients who had the luxury of iron-framed beds!

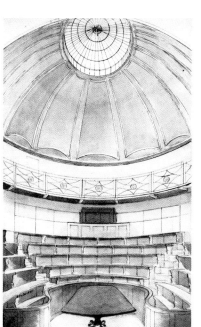

An important 18th century innovation was the introduction of operating theatres. These were on the top floor to ensure they received the maximum benefit from daylight. They had viewing terraces above the

Operating theatre

stage", the operating table. A male theatre was built above **Cutts** in 1751 and demolished in 1862. A female theatre was not built until 1821. It was adjacent to **Dorcas** and the tower of St Thomas's Church. This theatre survived the demolition of the Hospital and, in 1956, the bricked-up approach door was discovered with the theatre intact behind. It is now open, to all those who can manage the spiral staircase, as part of The Old Operating Theatre and Herb Garret Museum.

Henry Cline and Astley Cooper were two outstanding medical men working at St Thomas' at the turn of the 18th century.

Cline was an anatomist and surgeon and an inspirational teacher who, in 1784, had apprenticed Astley Cooper. He was rather wild when young but responded to the "great" Cline, working under him at St Thomas' for the next 16 years. In 1800, Astley Cooper joined the staff of Guy's and he too became a famous anatomist and surgeon. At that time bodies were needed for study. Many gravediggers joined the Resurrectionists,

digging up the recently buried and selling to the anatomists. This was a lucrative trade. When one of their number, Joseph Naples, was arrested, he was released following the intervention of Astley Cooper who was an important client. Cline and Astley Cooper were in the forefront of the campaign which led to the passing of the Anatomy Act in 1832. This Act made the supply of corpses for dissection legal, ending the trade of the Resurrectionists.

Naples was later employed in the dissecting room of St Thomas'. Despite the name similarity, there is no evidence of a connection between this Naples and the Naple's mentioned earlier.

Briefly, from 1817, **Regency** ward was opened to accommodate injured troops from the Napoleonic Wars. This ward may have been a change of use of the foul nurses' accommodation. Interestingly, at this time, the words "venereal disease" rather than the word "foul" are used in the Hospital Reports.

In the 1820s, St Thomas' physicians first permitted the surgeons to write prescriptions for their outpatients. It is possible that the Order of September 1687 "that the anciente rule be adhered to that noe surgeon shall give anie phisick to anie patient" has never been rescinded for inpatients.

In 1828 "The United Hospitals or Boro' Hospitals Club", a society to promote dining and discussion, was founded by the doctors of St Thomas' and Guy's. Following a rift the medical schools split in 1836. Despite this "The Boro' Club" flourished and continues to the present day. Although the medical schools went their separate ways, they were reunited in 1982.

The next 30 years, 1830 – 1860, saw many medical and social changes which had an impact on St Thomas'. In 1832 when taxes were reduced, the female ward windows were unblocked. In 1835 and 1842, when the female wards were rebuilt, the patients were accommodated in separate medical (**Anne** and **Mary**) and surgical (**Elizabeth** and **Dorcas**) wards. In 1849, Sister Clinical, a specialist nursing position, was created. Between 1847 and 1856, chloroform (followed by ether) was used for anaesthesia and eye surgery became a specialty.

At the same time as these changes, the railway companies were buying land near to the Hospital. The 1859 proposals for railway development would lead to St Thomas' having to be demolished. However, before demolition the hospital had an important role to play in the history of nursing.

With the full support of the Court of Governors and a dedicated fund of nearly £50,000, the Nightingale Training School for Nurses opened on 24 June 1860, aiming to make nursing a respectable profession for women.

Florence Nightingale had spent many years formulating her training strategy and selected Mrs Sarah Wardroper, Matron of St Thomas' since 1854, as Superintendent of the School.

The essence of the Nightingale approach was dedication and discipline. All probationers (students) and Nightingales (trained nurses) were residents in a nurses' home. Uniform was worn and a strict moral code enforced in an atmosphere which promoted the wellbeing of both nurses and patients. There were no vows, no certificates and no examinations. The ethos was to train, then go elsewhere and train others.

In January 1862, the Charing Cross Railway Bill was passed. A compulsory purchase order in favour of the South Eastern Railway Company was subsequently served and the Hospital was given six months to move.

1 Group of nurses, late 19th century

2 Florence Nightingale

SURREY GARDENS
1862 – 1871

The Governors found the Hospital a
temporary home in the derelict music hall and
zoological buildings at Surrey Gardens in
nearby Newington.

The main building was on two levels. The
upper level was partitioned to create four
wards, each containing 22 beds. A large male
accident ward was on the ground floor. There
was limited water, no ventilation or heating,
and the kitchens doubled as the operating
theatre. The Governors recognised the
importance of keeping the medical and
nursing schools as fully functional as possible
and so, despite the unsanitary conditions,
some residential accommodation was
provided in the zoological buildings. It is not
surprising that Nurse Rebecca Strong later
wrote of her experiences "confusion …
(regarding ward names)… was one of the
least of the evils".

1

2

A NEW HOSPITAL IN LAMBETH
1871 – 1900

Florence Nightingale greatly influenced the
design of the new St Thomas', as acknowledged by the architect, Henry Currey. In 1859
she had published the first edition of "Notes
on Hospitals", which included her thoughts
on how hospitals should be designed and
administered. She was a passionate strategist

3

and statistician rather than an innovator. Having seen Lariboisière Hospital outside Paris, she realised the importance of design for improved hygiene and health in hospitals. Her ideas had been adopted in the building of the new military hospital at Greenwich, the Herbert Hospital, opened in 1866. Florence Nightingale made meticulous calculations regarding dimensions and the efficient use of space. She appreciated the value of pavilion ward blocks with courtyards between. In the wards she proposed full height windows at specified intervals with the beds set between which facilitated ventilation and allowed air to circulate without creating draughts. She stipulated that clean and dirty areas should be separate so food and clean linen were stored at the ward entry with washing and sanitary facilities at the opposite end.

The Nightingale system of hospital and ward design with her comprehensive instructions for hospital management, were used nationally and internationally until the mid-20th century. The legacy of Florence Nightingale is that her ideas remain as valid today as at the time they were first proposed.

St Thomas' was rebuilt in Lambeth on an almost rectangular site narrowing towards the southern end. It extended from Westminster Bridge in the north to Lambeth Bridge in the south and was bounded by the River Thames to the west and Stangate and decrepit buildings to the east. Stangate was a paved causeway which led to an ancient ford. Its name was preserved with a small triangular garden (a gore) east of the hospital site being

1 Surrey Gardens interior, 1862 – 71

2 Surrey Gardens exterior

3 Architects' drawing, 1865

4 St Thomas' Hospital, Lambeth, view and plan 1870

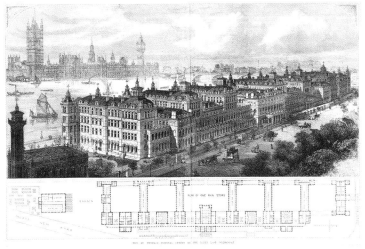

4

1

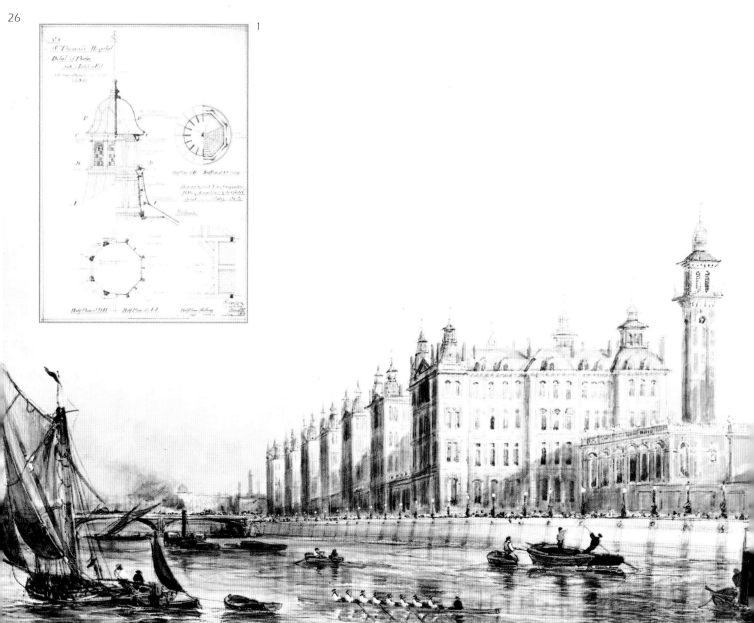

named Stangate Green. A new road was built, known today as Lambeth Palace Road. There were eight "blocks" with the medical school at the southern end.

Miss Nightingale attended neither the foundation stone setting in 1868, nor the glittering royal opening by Queen Victoria in 1871. Although in regular correspondence with many of her probationers and "Nightingales", she visited St Thomas' only once on 27 January 1882. She was received by The Matron, Mrs Sarah Wardroper, who wrote a few days later of the visit by "…our dearly beloved Chief … (to the) pretty Alexandra Ward … (and the) Nightingale Home … which has for more than twenty years borne your honoured name".

Block 1 was entered from Westminster Bridge Road and housed the administrative offices and the original Governors' Hall. Recent research has suggested that Monet painted several of his Houses of Parliament master-pieces from the balcony of this hall. Block 5 was the main entrance into Central Hall with the chapel above. The wards were in the other six blocks and all were named above the entry doors. Some biblical names had been dropped in order to honour Queen Victoria, Prince Albert and their nine children. By the end of the century wards were named to honour those who had worked to benefit St Thomas'. The total number of beds was about 550. Most wards had 14 beds along each of the long sides although there were fewer beds in **Ophthalmic** in Block 2 and **Dorcas**, **Anne**, **Luke**, **Lydia**, **William**, **Henry** and **Job** in Block 8.

3

1 Architects' detail drawing 1865
2 The Hospital from the river, late 1800s
3 The Hospital from the road 1871
4 Royal opening 1871

4

1

The female wards in Blocks 2, 3 and 4 were **Alice**, **Adelaide**, **Mary**, **Florence**, **Alexandra**, **Elizabeth**, **Beatrice**, **Magdalen**, **Victoria**, **Charity** and **Christian**.

The male wards in Blocks 6 and 7 were **Albert**, **Arthur**, **George**, **Alfred**, **Edward**, **Leopold** (changed to **Nuffield** in 1934) and **Clayton**.

Lack of funds prevented the commissioning of some wards. By 1873 the Governors were faced with serious financial difficulties. Over £90,000 had been borrowed to cover the building costs. Income had to cover local taxes and the day-to-day running costs. In 1880 the Ladies' Guild, now The Friends of St Thomas' Hospital, was formed to raise funds. A year later "paying patients" were admitted into **St Thomas' Home** aiming to further increase income. As a result of a well-supported appeal and large grants, all wards were open before the end of the century.

In preparation for the move to Lambeth, the Governors had decided to increase the senior medical staff from three physicians and three surgeons to four, each with three assistants. In addition there were specialist assistants for ophthalmology, dentistry, obstetrics and gynaecology, anaesthetics and, by the early 1880s, electrical therapy. This was the start of specialist departments with dedicated nursing staff and wards.

St Thomas' was known abroad as well as in the UK and was chosen by Röntgen for the first demonstration of x-rays in a London hospital. This was on 13 February 1896.

2

TWO WORLD WARS AND THE AFTERMATH 1900 TO 1960

In the next century, the reputation of the Hospital and its medical, dental and nursing schools continued to grow both at home and internationally. **Adelaide** (originally **Alfred** on the ground floor of Block 7) was refurbished to admit patients from the Casualty Department and renamed **City of London**. Electric lighting was installed and new operating theatres were built. The space freed between Blocks 2 and 3 became **Seymour** for children requiring surgery and, between Blocks 6 and 7, **Lilian** for children requiring medical treatment.

The hospital attracted highly talented students and staff. One such was Sister Ophthalmic, Minnie Randell. In 1911 she started the reorganisation of the Departments of Massage, Swedish Exercise and, later, Electrotherapy which, together, became the Department of Physical Therapy and the School of Physiotherapy. The first Medical Director was Dr J B Mennell who, during the First World War, pioneered the early mobilisation of soldiers who had fractures and other injuries. Mennell retired in 1935 and his successor, Rowley Bristow, allocated physiotherapists to specialist medical and surgical teams (firms), a practice which continues to this day. The School and Department of Occupational Therapy were opened in 1943.

During the First World War extra beds were needed for servicemen so six huts were erected. They were not named but the five which served as wards were allocated the letters A to E and the sixth was used for recreational purposes.

The years between the wars saw many changes at the Hospital. Badges for "Nightingales" were introduced. More building work took place. In 1927 **St Thomas' House** was opened as a medical students' residence. The recreational areas became the venue for many boisterous social events. In 2008 it

3

1 Beatrice Ward 1904
2 Stangate Green 1940s
3 Operating Theatre, early 20th century

became home to one of the medical school libraries and offices. **Riddell House** opened in 1936 as a new nurses' home. Despite sustaining severe bomb damage during the Second World War, the building was in use until 2002. It was then demolished to make way for the new **Evelina Children's Hospital** which opened in October 2005.

Preparations for war dominated August 1939. Basement rooms were converted into operating theatres and temporary wards. Contingency plans were formulated so that students could continue their training. "Blackout" precautions were installed. This national regulation was implemented to prevent enemy aircraft locating targets by lights.

There was concern that nurses coming off duty via the basement corridor under Block 6, using only their pocket torches, might walk into the brick wall. In an inspired action someone painted the wall with white rabbits and other animals – all well preserved today.

1

Although "blackout" was effective, nothing could prevent the River Thames from gleaming. At night it guided the Luftwaffe to London and St Thomas', located on the riverbank, was bombed. Ten members of staff were killed and others were wounded in the attacks but, incredibly, no patient was injured. A War Diary was kept by an unknown official which provides interesting information.

2

The first bomb fell on Block 1 and the adjacent Gassiot House on 9 September 1940. Two nurses and four physiotherapists were killed. Next day **Nuffield** moved into the basement of Block 2 and **Lilian** into a small basement classroom, but within three days all

the ground and first floor wards had reopened. The bombing of 13 September 1940 caused no deaths but badly damaged **Jericho**, the night nurses' home.

On 15 September 1940 a large bomb hit the Hospital adjacent to Central Hall. It penetrated the basement corridor, killing two house surgeons and a nurse. Forty-two staff were injured, one of whom died later. Next day all inpatients were evacuated. Another hit made it necessary to close the Hospital for a short time. Temporary repairs were undertaken and St Thomas' became an efficient 50-bedded emergency unit. The fourth large bomb which fell on 15 October 1940 badly damaged the telephone exchange and **City of London**. More beds were urgently needed so the

1 White Rabbit wall

2 & 4 Bomb damage 15 September 1940

3 Bomb on Nightingale Home 16 April 1941

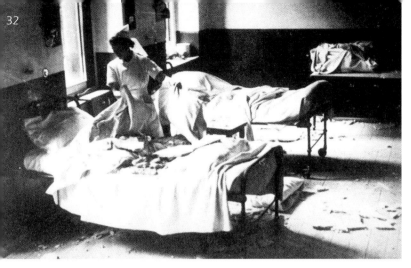

"the most severe raid we had yet experienced" and two firemen died in the explosions. Despite the fires, **Arthur** was kept open and **Scutari** was able to accommodate patients the next day.

Although many of the wards were closed during the war, some of their names were kept "open". Early in 1941 the Governors accepted the lease of Hydestile Hospital near Godalming. Although the facility was largely a series of huts, it remained part of St Thomas' until it closed in 1968. The 36 bedded wards included **Victoria** (for female surgical patients), **Florence** and **Anne** (female medical patients) and **Lilian** for children. The men's wards were later named after Sir Arthur **Stanley** and the eminent surgeon **George Makins**. When the wards were reopened at St Thomas', Hydestile retained all the names except **Lilian**, which became **America**.

Repair of buildings and relocation of the various schools and support facilities were priorities at the end of the war. In 1948, the NHS came into being.

basement bed store was converted into a ward and named **Scutari**. The rough stone walls and basic facilities reminded the staff of the infamous Barrack Hospital where Florence Nightingale had worked for 20 months during the Crimean War. **Scutari** is now part of the Department of Psychiatry.

Following six months of "light" bombing which caused minimal damage, the fifth large bomb fell on 16 April 1941. **Nuffield** and **Arthur** had to be evacuated although new casualties were admitted to **Scutari** and other basement areas. The night of 10 May 1941 was recorded as

1 Temporary ward in the basement in the early 1940s

2 Evacuation of patients 1941

The management and funding of the Hospital ceased to be under the sole control of the Board of Governors. The medical school was separately managed and financed. The last Board meeting was held on 20 May 1948. At this time there were 501 beds at St Thomas', including the newest six-bedded **Holden** (opposite **George**) for patients of the metabolic and endocrine unit.

St Thomas' was designated as a "Teaching Hospital Unit" with management responsibility for five other hospitals and a total of 982 beds. The geographical spread of the Unit raised logistical issues, particularly communication problems. These were significantly alleviated by Peter Styles when he was working in the Electronics Department at St Thomas'.

In 1954 he invented, in conjunction with Multitone Electronics, the world's first "bleep" paging system.

Despite new management arrangements the Governors remained proud of St Thomas' longstanding traditions and values. They applied for and were granted a new Coat of Arms as those of the City of London were no longer appropriate. This included two birds – a chough (popularly known as the Becket bird) and a nightingale.

The 1950s wards had 31 beds – 15 on each side and one bed in a side ward for patients needing special care. Blocks 1 and 2 were closed. In Block 3 the wards **Alexandra**, **Elizabeth** and **Beatrice** and, in Block 4, the wards **Florence**, **Charity** and **Christian** were female wards. **Albert**, **Arthur**, **George** and **Holden** in Block 6 and **Edward**, **Nuffield**, **Clayton** and **City** in Block 7 were male wards. In Block 8 **Luke** was for patients with tuberculosis and **William** and **Henry** for female and male thoracic patients respectively. Above these were **Mary 1** and **Mary 2**, the "lying-in" (maternity) wards. At that time most surgical patients were in hospital for two weeks and so too were women in the maternity unit.

There are many famous alumni of St Thomas' but Cicely Saunders deserves a specific mention. She qualified as a "Nightingale" in 1944 and as an almoner in 1947. Almoners had been appointed from the Governors since 1557 "for the daily oversight of the house". From 1905 onwards, Lady Almoners were trained evolving into, in the 1960s, Medical Social Workers. To fulfill her ambition of improving care for the terminally ill, Cicely Saunders undertook yet more training. As a qualified medical doctor she founded St Christopher's Hospice in Sydenham, south London, in 1967. Her approach to the care of the dying has since been introduced worldwide for both adults and children. She was created Dame in 1979 and died in 2005 aged 87. There is no ward named after her, nor after the 1960s Matron Theodora Turner. But both are honoured with busts in Central Hall adjacent to the statue of Florence Nightingale.

In 1974, the charitable funds of St Thomas', which had been retained in 1948 as a condition of St Thomas' becoming part of the NHS, were passed to the custodianship of a separate registered charity, the Special Trustees for St Thomas' Hospital. These funds are now under the control of the Guy's and St Thomas' Charity whose grant has funded this book.

EAST WING 1966 – 2008

In the early 1960s, land to the east of the original St Thomas' Hospital site was purchased. Lambeth Palace Road was diverted and an entirely new hospital was planned to accommodate 900 inpatients. There would be outpatient departments with support facilities and accommodation for the training schools. However, a shortage of funds prevented the plans from being implemented in full and the remaining Nightingale blocks were not demolished. This was fortunate for London's architectural heritage, as, due to the changed attitudes of the 1970s, the 1871 "Nightingale" blocks are now Grade II listed buildings.

2

3

1 Theodora Turner 1960s
2 Aerial view 1950 – the original Lambeth Palace Road
3 Aerial view 1963 – rerouting of Lambeth Palace Road

Construction was to be in three stages. Stage one accommodated the Casualty Department and wards and was named the East Wing. It was opened in June 1966. There was one ward on each floor. Beds were in four or six-bedded bays, with piped oxygen and nurse call buttons at each bed. Each floor had a day room (an innovation in patient welfare), a teaching room for students and, in the bath rooms, special "high baths" which were meant to help nurses. Unfortunately they proved impossible for patients to climb into! Another innovation was the creation of the Central Sterile Supply Department which did away with the noisy ward-based sterilisers.

On the first floor, **Lloyd Still** for psychiatric inpatients was adjacent to the outpatients department, **Scutari**. Above was **Mead**, the intensive treatment unit (ITU), pioneered by Dr Ron Bradley. **Doulton**, for male orthopaedic patients was on the fourth floor and **Becket** for female orthopaedic patients on the fifth. On the sixth floor **Wardroper** was the thoracic surgery ward for female patients. The seventh floor housed offices whilst the male thoracic surgery ward, **Cheselden**, was on the eighth floor. On the ninth floor was **Florence** for female medical patients. **Simon** on the tenth floor had 20 rooms for paying patients.

Ward Sisters were generally given one week's notice of impending moves but not so the current Sister Charity. In 1967 she received one day's notice of **Charity's** move to **City of London**. She achieved this without mislaying a patient, nurse or her old ward's name as she adopted the title of Sister City of Charity.

Medical advances and administrative changes since the East Wing was built have led to changes in name and ward use. "Cas" (Casualty) is now A&E (Accident and Emergency). On the first and second floors is the Intensive Care Unit (ICU). Floors three to nine are the Cardio-Thoracic Centre with the wards: **Evan Jones**, **Becket**, **Stephen**, **Doulton** and **Sarah Swift**. On the tenth floor is **Victoria** for patients admitted from A&E. The IT Department is on the top floor.

NORTH WING 1976 – 2008

In 1963 the architect Eugene Rosenberg was commissioned to design stage two of the redevelopment, comprising the 13-storey North Wing, Gassiot House and a 5-storey outpatient block. Stage two was officially opened by HM Queen Elizabeth II on 11 November 1976.

The North Wing is typical of its time: a square building with the main lifts and stairs in the middle and service stairs and lifts in each corner.

Rosenberg was once heard to say that there should be a museum at St Thomas' celebrating the life and legacy of Florence Nightingale. This comment, and the 1978 discovery of a box of artefacts which had belonged to her, led to the building of the museum under Gassiot House. The Florence Nightingale Museum was opened in 1989 and thrives today as an important resource for academic research as well as being a popular attraction, with visitors from near and far.

The North Wing had wards on floors six to 12 inclusive. The ward names were selected in 1973 and were a mixture of old and new. There have been many changes in the names and uses of these wards over the years. Initially, there were 630 beds. Most patients were in four or six-bedded bays but there were also two or three single-bedded side rooms for isolation nursing. A modern facility was the Hospital's Radio Becket with headphone access for all patients.

Aerial view 1977 showing the completed new hospital site

In 1976, **Adelaide** and **Grosvenor**, the gynaecological wards, were on the sixth floor. **Louise** and **Holden** also opened on this floor in the 1980s. The maternity wards, **Haydon West**, **Haydon East** and **Mary**, the Special Care Baby Unit and teaching facilities for the newly created Guy's and St Thomas' School of Midwifery were on the seventh floor. The children's wards **Lilian** (medical), **Seymour** (surgical) and **Helen** (general) and the **Royal Eye** ward were on the floor above. On the ninth floor were the surgical wards **Alexandra** (female), **Nightingale** (male) and the medical wards **Henry** (male) and **Anne** (female). On the tenth floor were the renal wards **Page** (male) and **Alice** (female) and the genito-urinary wards **Stanley** (male) and **Victoria** (female).

On the 11th floor were **Bristow** and **Elizabeth** for male and female medical patients respectively and **Evan Jones** and **Beatrice**, the male and female cardiothoracic/cardiology wards. On the 12th floor **Mitchiner**, **Howard** and **Gullan** admitted private patients. There was also **Hillyers** for staff and the Nurses' Sick Floor suite.

In 1970 the first male student Leslie Graham was accepted for nurse training. He qualified as a Nightingale in 1974.

In past centuries women had used the title "Mrs" to denote respectability but, as recently as the 1960s, a Deputy Matron had to resign when she married. However, by the early 1970s, students and nurses who married could continue in post. The requirement for nurses to be practising Anglicans was also abolished bringing nursing at St Thomas' in line with 20th century attitudes.

As previously mentioned, in 1982 the Medical and Dental Schools of Guy's and St Thomas' were reunited as the United Medical and Dental Schools (UMDS). When, in 1998, UMDS became part of King's College London (KCL), the Guy's site was the main academic campus for medical and dental students.

In a separate move the Nightingale Training School for Nurses was closed in 1996. Nurse training transferred to KCL when the Florence

Nightingale School of Nursing and Midwifery was established.

Since the North Wing was built there has been considerable change in the way healthcare is provided and consequently on the use of the wards. Today, many patients are treated as "day cases" and do not require beds. Specialist nurse practitioners perform procedures previously undertaken by doctors and admission is not needed.

The final set of Nightingale students, Autumn 1992 – the last set to receive the Nightingale badge on completion of their training.

As part of infection control measures staff who come into direct contact with patients have arms bare below the elbow. The wearing of white coats by doctors which ceased for several years was reintroduced in 2008. All nurses (except midwives) have always worn uniforms and, in 2005 new designs were introduced. Dresses or tunics and trousers are of specific colours which indicate the nurse's grade.

From the perspective of this book, a surprising change is the dropping of ward names on the Women's Services units.

In 2000 the sixth, seventh and part of the eighth floors were closed for two years and underwent major refurbishment. Today on the sixth floor are 39 **Post Natal** beds and the **Lansdell Suite** for six private patients. Two **SANDS** beds, the **Home from Home** delivery unit and the **Hospital Birth Centre** are on the seventh floor. On the eighth floor are **Gynaecology** the Ophthalmic Day Surgery Unit and **Nightingale** with 24 beds for patients awaiting transfer to another ward. On the ninth floor are **Mark** with 26 beds for stroke patients and **Henry**, **Anne** and **Alexandra**, each providing care for 28 elderly patients.

1

On the tenth floor are **Luke** (vascular surgery) and **William Gull** and **Albert** which are both general medical wards. **Albert** was the last Nightingale-style ward. It was closed in June 2005 to the regret of many. Patients had little privacy but as nurses said "we could easily check every patient and patients could always see us".

There are four wards on the 11th floor. **Alan Apley** for orthopaedic and plastic surgery patients and **George Perkins** for orthopaedic patients each has 28 beds. **Northumberland** and **Page** are for patients undergoing abdominal surgery. Each has 20 beds and a four-bedded high dependency unit. On the 12th floor specialist nurse practitioners treat outpatients in **Mitchiner**. **Westminster** Unit is the private patients' suite and includes **Howard**. **Gullan** is a day care unit for dermatology patients and **Hillyers** has 18 beds for patients with HIV or dermatological conditions.

2

SOUTH WING 1979 – 2008

The planned third stage of the redevelopment was abandoned, largely due to a lack of funds. The buildings received Grade II listing. In 1976 **Mary 1** and **Mary 2** in Block 8 were renamed **Wrigley** and **Garland**. The Chapel and Governors' Hall were refurbished. Wards were gradually closed as the design of the buildings made them unsuitable for modern inpatient care. The space was converted for outpatient and administrative use.

In 2008 the Sharpington Staff Club and Shepherd Hall are open. So too is the **Adamson** Centre which provides psychiatric services. Within the centre, the names **Scutari**, **Lloyd Still** and **Elizabeth** have been retained.

1 New designs for uniforms 2005
2 St Thomas' Chapel

Also still open in this Wing are **Lane-Fox** (the respiratory and sleep disorders unit) and the office of the Dreadnought Seamen's Hospital.

THE FUTURE

St Thomas' has survived 900 years, moving from its religious foundation to secular independence. Today it provides the majority of the acute medical and surgical services for the Guy's and St Thomas' NHS Foundation Trust. Recent innovations include the Medicinema charity's cinema for patients. Renovation of the old medical school is planned.

Medicinema

The future is bright and further development certain. Change is an important element of life for which St Thomas' is well equipped.

THE WARDS OF
ST THOMAS' HOSPITAL

Dates at the end of an entry indicate when the ward name was first used and if the ward is open, or when the name was last used.

ABDIEL

Abdiel was a biblical clan leader who trusted in God and won many battles. The name had symbolic significance. **(1638 – probably 1701)**

ABRAHAM

Abraham was the first biblical Patriarch. He strove to obey the will of God and faced many trials, including offering his only child, Isaac, as a sacrifice. At the critical moment, God showed Abraham a ram caught in a nearby thicket and accepted instead the animal as a sacrifice. The name was a symbolic example to the sick poor.
(1583 – 1862)

ADAMSON

Edward James Adamson (1911 – 1996) pioneered art therapy for the mentally ill. He was a conscientious objector in the Second World War and taught art in the Army Medical Corps. He believed that painting treated the war-damaged mind. He founded the British Association of Art Therapists and was renowned as an artist, therapist and teacher. He remained active until he died.
(2000 – open in 2008)

ADELAIDE

The ward could have been named after Queen Adelaide the wife of William IV (1792 – 1849) or after Victoria Adelaide, the Princess Royal (1840 – 1901), the first-born child of Queen Victoria and Prince Albert. She married the German Emperor Frederick III and, after his death in 1888, became known as the Empress Frederick. However, there is a third royal Adelaide, Duchess of Teck (1833 – 1897) a granddaughter of George III. She was concerned to improve the welfare of the poor and is the most probable "nominee" for this choice of ward name. Her only daughter, Mary, would marry the future George V.
(1871 – 2000)

ALAN APLEY

Alan Graham Apley (1914 – 1996) is acknowledged as the greatest teacher of

orthopaedics in the English language.

He trained at University College Hospital in London, qualifying just before the Second World War. Following service in the Royal Army Medical Corps, he was appointed to the Rowley Bristow Orthopaedic in 1947. For almost the next 50 years he devised and ran the Orthopaedic Course for the Fellowship of the Royal College of Surgeons. Twice every year, approximately 100 trainee surgeons participated. His course notes formed the basis of his most important textbook "A System of Orthopaedics and Fractures", first published in 1959. This ran to seven editions in his lifetime. He regarded the "pirate" version as an accolade. The book continues as "Apley's System…" in posthumous editions. In 1974 he was appointed Director of the Department of Orthopaedic Surgery at St Thomas'. He was in demand worldwide as a lecturer, being renowned for clarity and humour. Apley was elected Vice President by the Council of the Royal College of Surgeons of England. He retired in 1979 but for the next ten years was Editor of the British edition of the Journal of Bone and Joint Surgery. **(1998 – open in 2008)**

ALBERT

Albert was named after Queen Victoria's German husband, Albert of Saxe-Coburg-Gotha (1819 – 1861). They married in 1840. The couples were cousins, their mothers being sisters. They had nine children, all of whom married into other royal families in Europe. The Prince Consort became popular with the British. His interest in economic progress and culture led to the Great Exhibition of 1851. Albert died in 1861, probably of typhoid fever. Victoria was in mourning for the rest of her life. **(1871 – open in 2008)**

ALEXANDRA

Alexandra was probably named after the popular Danish wife (1844 – 1925) of Edward, Prince of Wales. They married in 1863 and in 1901 he succeeded his mother, Queen Victoria. On Edward VII's death, Alexandra was given the courtesy title Queen Mother.
(1871 – open in 2008)

ALFRED

Alfred was named after the fourth child of Queen Victoria and Prince Albert. Alfred (1844 – 1900) was a career sailor who, in early 1867, sailed around the world. In 1874 he married a daughter of the Russian Tsar. In 1893 he inherited from his uncle to take the title Duke of Saxe-Coburg and Gotha.
(1871 – 1880)

ALICE

Alice was named after the third child of Queen Victoria and Prince Albert. Alice (1843 – 1878) nursed her father during his last illness in 1861. In 1862 she married into the family of Hesse. Prince Philip, Duke of Edinburgh is her great grandson. She was founder of a union which supported improvement in nursing services to the armed forces. In 1878 she died of diphtheria.
(1871 – 1980s)

ANNE

Queen Anne (1665 – 1714) reigned from 1702 until 1714. The younger daughter of James II, she married Prince George of Denmark in 1683. During her reign she showed some interest in St Thomas' thus making it appropriate to name a ward after her. Despite 18 pregnancies, only five of Anne's children survived birth. Her only surviving son died aged 11 in 1700. This tragic story ensured that Anne was the last of the Stuart monarchs. Conforming to the 1701 Act of Settlement, her successor was the Protestant German Prince George of Hanover.
(1708 – open in 2008)

APLEY

See Alan Apley

ARTHUR

Arthur (1850 – 1942) was the third son of

Queen Victoria and Prince Albert. He was a career soldier. From 1882 until 1942 he was President of St Thomas' Hospital, thus ending the tradition of appointing Presidents from the City of London Corporation. He was Governor General of Canada from 1911 – 1916 and Grand Master of the Freemasons from 1903 until 1940. **(1871 – 1986)**

BATEMAN

See Thomas Bateman

BEATRICE

Beatrice (1857 – 1944) was the youngest of Queen Victoria and Prince Albert's children. She was secretary to her mother for the last 40 years of Victoria's life. She later edited, re-wrote and destroyed her mother's diaries in accordance with the Queen's wishes. In 1885 Beatrice married Prince Henry of Battenburg and the couple lived with the widowed Queen. Henry died of a fever in 1896. Beatrice was President of the Isle of Wight branch of the British Red Cross. **(1871 – 1998)**

BECKET

Thomas Becket (1118 – 1170) was created Archbishop of Canterbury by his friend King Henry II.

The pair quarrelled frequently when Becket became Archbishop. When Henry was heard to say "who will rid me of this turbulent priest?" four knights took this literally and murdered Becket in Canterbury Cathedral. Henry did public penance for this deed.

Within three years, Becket was made a saint and many priories changed their name in his honour. St Mary Overie became St Thomas'. Closed in 1540 as a consequence of Henry VIII's dissolution of the monasteries, when reopened in 1552 it was dedicated to St Thomas the Apostle. However the Becket association has never been forgotten. When St Thomas' was awarded a new Coat of Arms in 1948, it featured a chough, or "Becket bird", in his honour. **(1966 – open in 2008)**

BOWES

Robert Kenneth Bowes (1904 – 1958) trained in Liverpool, qualifying in 1929. He joined the staff of the obstetric and gynaecology department at St Thomas' in 1931 and was, unusually, appointed consultant in 1936 without taking the examinations of the Royal College of Surgeons. He was eventually elected member and fellow in 1955. Bowes advocated Caesarian Section to prevent foetal problems but always with the mother's welfare in mind. From 1948 until his premature death following surgery, Bowes worked with Garland and Wrigley at the Grosvenor Hospital for Women which was part of the St Thomas' Hospital group. **(1976 – 1980s)**

BRAXTON HICKS

John Braxton Hicks (1823 – 1897) entered Guy's medical school in 1841 and practised as a physician at both Guy's and St Mary's Hospitals. His name was given to a normal phenomenon of pregnancy he first described in 1872 when painless "false" contractions, less acute on exercise, are experienced weeks before the baby is due. **(1990s – 2000)**

BRISTOW

As a student at St Thomas', Walter Rowley Bristow (1882 – 1947) was renowned for his sporting ability and love of the new motor car. He became a fine teacher and surgeon. Bristow qualified in 1907 and served in Gallipoli in the First World War. In 1920 he joined the orthopaedic team at St Thomas', remaining there until he retired in 1946. He founded and was Director of St Nicholas and St Martin Orthopaedic Hospital in Pyrford, Surrey which, following his death, was renamed the Rowley Bristow Orthopaedic Hospital in his honour. **(1976 – 1997)**

CHARITY

The reason for this choice of name is unknown. It is strange that Princess Louise the sixth child of Queen Victoria and Prince Albert had no ward named after her. Charity may have been her choice. Alternatively, it has been suggested that the biblical lines from 1 Corinthians 13:1 which end "…but the greatest of these is Charity" were the inspiration for the name. Charity was a reminder to all of the constant need of both

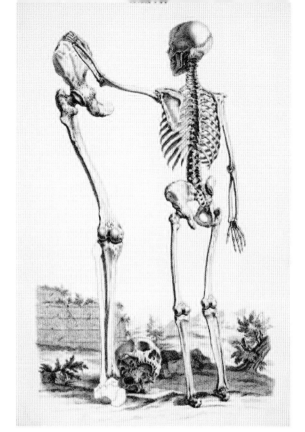

funds and volunteers in order to provide free treatment for the sick poor. **(1871 – 1973)**

CHESELDEN

William Cheselden (1688 – 1752) was a surgeon at St Thomas' from 1718 to 1738. Cheselden was a skilled anatomist and published *Anatomy of the Bones* and *Anatomy of the Human Body.*

He had great skill in eye surgery, lithotomy (the removal of stones) and amputation. In the days before anaesthesia, speed and accuracy were the most important skills for a surgeon.

He was recognisable by the turban he wore rather than the fashionable powdered wig (see page 19). Cheselden was in the forefront of the movement to separate the surgeons from the Barbers' Company. This he achieved in 1745 with the formation of the Company of Surgeons which became the Royal College of Surgeons of England. **(1966 – 1997)**

CHRISTIAN

Christian was named after Queen Victoria and Prince Albert's fifth child, Helena (1846 – 1923). When she married she took the title Princess Christian of Schleswig Holstein. The couple lived in England and throughout her life she was concerned with nurse training and patient care. **(1871 – 1973)**

CITY OF LONDON

City of London was the name given to the ground floor ward of Block 7 which was refurbished with a grant from the City of London. Since the Charter granted by Edward VI in 1553, the Governors of St Thomas' had come from the City of London livery companies. These wealthy individuals both donated and raised funds in support of the Hospital. (1898 – 1970s)

CLAYTON

Sir Robert Clayton (1629 – 1707) was the immensely wealthy President of the Governors from 1692 to 1707. The son of a Northamptonshire farmer, he was the beneficiary of several fortunes. Clayton succeeded to a Baronetcy in 1669 and his portrait was painted by several famous artists. He was Lord Mayor of London in 1679 – 80. His marble statue, created by the famous wood carver Grinling Gibbons, stood in the third court of the Southwark site and today stands in the grounds of St Thomas' in Lambeth - with replacement hands after having regularly been damaged by celebrating students. (1871 – 1979)

CLINICAL

Clinical was opened during the 1849 cholera epidemic. Probably a clinical space was hastily converted for temporary use, as no location is mentioned in the Governors' Reports. **(1849)**

CUTTS

The ward was named after the surgical procedure. Cutting out bladder stones (lithotomy) was one of the earliest specialist surgical procedures. **(1701 – 1862)**

DORCAS

Dorcas (Tabitha) was a biblical disciple of Peter who miraculously revived her when she died. She was particularly concerned with the welfare of babies, young children and widows, making garments for, and donating them to, the poor. The present-day Dorcas Society also undertakes this charitable work.
(1638 – 1950)

DOULTON

In 1860 Henry Doulton started manufacturing decorative porcelain and tiles at his Lambeth pottery factory. In 1898 Doulton produced the reredos and the Wardroper Memorial for the St Thomas' Chapel. He was then commissioned to make the famous nursery rhyme tiles for the two new children's wards Lilian and Seymour. The factory closed in 1956 but the ornate entrance facade still stands in Black Prince Road.
(1966 – open in 2008)

3

EDWARD (IN SOUTHWARK)

Edward (in Southwark) was almost certainly named after Edward VI (1537 – 1553). He was the son of Lady Jane Seymour (third wife of King Henry VIII) and was always in poor health. On his father's death (1547) Edward's uncle Edward Seymour was appointed Lord Protector of England but it was Edward VI who restored St Thomas', granting the Royal Hospitals Charter in 1552.
(1734 – 1862)

1 City of London ward c. 1900
2 Sir Robert Clayton
3 Doulton's Dick Whittington tile

EDWARD (IN LAMBETH)

Edward (in Lambeth) was named after the second child of Queen Victoria and Prince Albert. Edward (1841 – 1910) was heir apparent for 60 years before reigning as Edward VII. As a young man he enjoyed his education but, after his marriage in 1863 to the Danish Princess Alexandra, he acquired the reputation of being a playboy and of having many mistresses. He was, however, serious about his royal responsibilities. He was a freemason (Grand Master from 1875) and helped found the Royal College of Music. In 1901 Edward became the first and only monarch of the House of Saxe-Coburg as his son, George V, adopted the title House of Windsor as a reaction to the rising tensions between England and Germany prior to the First World War. **(1871 – 1979)**

ELIZABETH

Elizabeth was named after Queen Elizabeth I (1533 – 1603), daughter of King Henry VIII and his second wife, the ill-fated Anne Boleyn who was executed in 1536. Elizabeth was known as the Virgin Queen. She was wilful,

1

quick-tempered and determined – characteristics traditionally thought appropriate for her bright auburn hair. She was well educated, a linguist and enjoyed art and literature. During her reign Catholic Spain was overcome with the destruction of their Armada and England became the major power. **(1708 – 2007)**

EVAN JONES

Evan Jones (1907 – 1969) trained at St Thomas' Hospital, becoming consultant physician at the early age of 30. A legendary diagnostician, he was renowned for his encyclopaedic knowledge, his superlative

2

memory and Celtic intuition. Evan Jones was senior cardiologist at St Thomas' and was loved by patients for the clarity of his explanations. **(1976 – open in 2008)**

FAITH

It is not known why the name was chosen but is an apt choice. The sick poor needed faith in those tending them and the institution needed faith of continued support from benefactors. It is possible that Faith was politically inspired as the name was introduced at the time of Cromwell's puritanical rule.
(1646 – circa 1700)

FLORENCE

It was not considered respectable in the 19th century for well-educated, middle-class women, such as Florence Nightingale (1820 – 1910) to undertake paid work or seek training.

She dedicated her life to alleviating the plight of the sick poor and women trapped in the rituals of elegant society.

Florence Nightingale was a formidable

statistician, strategist and campaigner. The advent of her Nightingale Training School for Nurses in June 1860 led to training and a career structure for nurses. From 1858 she influenced dramatic health and hospital reforms within the army. She also influenced civil hospital design and administration, established district nursing and health visiting as professions, and assisted in the establishment of the British Red Cross Society, the Institute of Midwifery, rehabilitation services and much else that improved public health throughout the world. Her legacy is relevant today. **(1871 – 1999)**

FLORENCE NIGHTINGALE

See Florence and Nightingale

FOX

See Lane-Fox

1 Morning Prayers in Elizabeth Ward 1960
2 Nightingale Home Dining Room, c. 1900

GARLAND

Gordon Willie Garland (1919 – 1967) began his working life as an administration clerk at Guy's Hospital. However, in 1938 he entered Guy's medical school, qualifying in 1944. After wartime army service he returned to Guy's and in 1955 was appointed to the staff at St Thomas'. Widely respected as a teacher and for his administrative skills, he also worked at the Grosvenor Hospital with Bowes and Wrigley. Garland wrote a textbook "Obstetrics and Gynaecology" which is in print today. He suffered from asthma and the effects of cortico-steroid therapy led to his premature death. **(1976 – 1980s)**

GEORGE

George was named after either George I or II. George I (1660 – 1727) reigned from 1714 to 1727. His English was poor and he relied on his Prime Minister, Sir Robert Walpole. George II (1683 – 1760) reigned from 1727 to 1760 and was renowned for his mistresses and the bitter arguments he had with his father, his son and Sir Robert Walpole. **(1741 – 1986)**

GEORGE PERKINS

George Perkins (1892 – 1979) qualified at St Thomas' Hospital and spent his career in the Hospital except for the two World War periods in which he served with distinction. He was appointed as an orthopaedic surgeon in 1929 and, in 1948, he became the first Professor of Surgery at St Thomas'. In the 1940s, fractures of the femur were treated by putting the injured leg in traction, forcing patients to be inactive. Perkins argued that movement helped bones to heal and devised the "Perkins bed" with a hinged foot end. This enabled the patient to exercise the knee joint, under supervision, which expedited recovery. **(1976 – open in 2008)**

GREAT WARDS

The reason for this appellation is unknown. The wards were King's, Queen's, Jonas, Magdalen, Nightlayers and Noah. **(1550s – late 1600s)**

GROSVENOR

Grosvenor is the family name of the Dukes of Westminster who own land in Pimlico, London.

William Gros Veneur arrived in England as master of the hunt to William the Conqueror. In 1865 the Grosvenor Dispensary for Women and Children was opened and in 1895, the new Grosvenor Hospital was built on land donated from the estate. With the advent of the NHS in 1948, the Grosvenor, although north of the river, became part of St Thomas' group and was the main gynaecology training unit. The hospital closed in 1976 when the unit moved into the new North Wing of St Thomas'. **(1976 – 2003)**

GULL

see William Gull: Guy's list

GULLAN

Marion Agnes Gullan (1873 – 1958) trained at University College Hospital and was appointed Sister in the Nightingale Training School in 1914 by Matron Alicia Lloyd Still. These two nurses created the role of "Sister Tutor", a post Miss Gullan held for 20 years. A popular and capable lecturer, her 1920 textbook 'The Theory and Practice of Nursing" was considered indispensable. She and Miss Lloyd

Still also developed the nurses' training programme. In 1925 Miss Gullan was made an Honorary Nightingale and was presented with the new Nightingale badge. She died in St Thomas'. **(1976 – 2008)**

GYNAECOLOGY

In 1976 the gynaecological wards at St Thomas' were named Adelaide, Grosvenor and Louise. These wards became Braxton Hicks during the 1990s, a name they retained until 2000 when the women's units moved temporarily into Guy's during the renovations of St Thomas' North Wing. In 2003 the wards returned to St Thomas' but were renamed Gynaecology. **(2003 – open in 2008)**

HAYDON

Marion Olive Haydon, known as Sister Olive (circa 1870 - 1930) was the first midwife Tutor and, for many years, Head Midwife at the General Lying-in Hospital (GLI) in York Road, a few hundred yards from St Thomas'. She passed the London Obstetrical Society

Sister Olive Haydon

examination in 1901, was on the first Midwives Roll of 1904, designed the first midwives' teacher training course and was a proud Suffragist. She retired in 1926 and died suddenly in 1930. Within four years, an annual Haydon Memorial Lecture was organised which ran until 1976. In 1960 a GLI ward was named Haydon. In 1971 the GLI was closed and its services, and later the ward name, transferred to St Thomas'.
(GLI 1960 – 1971; STH 1971 – 2000)

HELEN

Helen was named after Princess Helena (1861 – 1922) of Pyrmont, Germany who, in 1882, married Prince Leopold, the youngest son of Queen Victoria and Prince Albert. He died early and she remarried and returned to Germany but later moved back to England. In 1905 she opened the Royal Waterloo Hospital for Children and Women.
(RWH 1905 – 1976; STH 1976 – 2000)

HENRY

The Governors' Reports of July 1782 note the name Henry was given to a ward previously named Susannah. It is highly unlikely that the ward was named after Henry II or Henry VIII.

However, in the late 1760s, Henry Cline (senior) (1750 – 1827), was apprenticed to a St Thomas' surgeon. From 1770 Cline gave anatomy and surgery lectures and in 1781 was appointed to the post of lecturer. In 1784 he was elected surgeon to the hospital, resigning in 1812. He was a popular student and a brilliant teacher. It is possible that the ward was nicknamed Henry's ward and the name stuck. Cline was both Master (1815) and, when the title was changed, President (1823) of the College of Surgeons of England.
(1782 – open in 2008)

HILLYERS

Hillyers was named after Gladys Verena Hillyers (1888 – 1948). She entered the Nightingale Training School in 1914, was a gold medallist and in 1924 became Sister in Charge of the training school. In 1927 she was joint first recipient of the Diploma of Nursing and in 1930 won a Rockefeller Scholarship to study in the USA. A brilliant administrator and supremely calm under pressure, her retirement from the post of Hospital Matron and Superintendent (1937 – 45) was delayed to enable her to steer the hospital and the training schools of nursing and physiotherapy through to the end of the Second World War. She was awarded the OBE in 1942. **(1976 – open in 2008)**

HOLDEN

Holden was named as a result of a bequest from Leila Holden in 1948 in memory of her sister who had been a patient of the newly-formed metabolic and endocrine unit. In the 1970s the name was given to a four-bedded bay in Louise Ward in the North Wing. **(1948 – 1988)**

HOWARD

The Hon Sir Arthur Howard (1896 – 1971) was Treasurer of St Thomas' jointly from 1943 to 1946 and then solely until 1964. He was Mayor of Westminster in 1937, Alderman (1945 – 1965), Council Leader (1954 – 1958) and MP for Westminster (1945 – 1950). **(1976 – open in 2008)**

ISAAC

In the Bible story Isaac was the son of Abraham and the second patriarch. Isaac was deceived by his son, Jacob, but forgave him. Sickness was often associated with sinning. This name had symbolic meaning for the sick poor. **(1583 – 1862)**

JACOB

Jacob was the biblical son of Isaac whom he deceived. He fled from home and was later himself deceived but finally felt able to return home. On the journey he won a fight with an angel who touched Jacob on his upper thigh

Jacob wrestling with the Angel by Eugène Delacroix (1861) © Gloumouth1

which shrivelled. This part of an animal is thus considered by Jews to be unclean meat i.e. not kosher. Jacob was the third patriarch and the fight was considered a sign of God's blessing. The name had symbolic meaning for the sick poor. **(1583 – 1862)**

JOB

Job was an Old Testament believer whose faith was tested by God with the deaths of his children, his servants and his livestock and a dreadful skin disease. Job trusted in God. His belief and fortitude was an example to the sick poor. **(1576 – early 1960s)**

JONAH

See Jonas

JONAS

Jonas (Jonah) was one of the six Great Wards. In the Bible story Jonas attempted to avoid serving God and was swallowed by a whale. He survived and repented and worked for his God. The name had symbolic significance. **(1576 – mid 1700s)**

JONES

See Evan Jones

JUDITH

In the Bible story Judith saved Judea from the Assyrians by seducing and then killing the enemy general Holofernes. To the sick poor she was a symbolic example of the power of courage in adversity. **(1576 – circa 1700)**

KING'S

King's was one of the six Great Wards of St Thomas' Spital. It was named after King Edward VI (1537 – 1553), the son of King Henry VIII and his third wife Jane Seymour. Edward was known as the "boy king" and was the first Protestant ruler of England. Due to his youth, the country was governed by the Regency Council. In 1553 he signed the Royal Charter which formalised the 1552 reopening of St Thomas'. **(circa 1553 – 1862)**

LANE-FOX

Felicity Lane-Fox (1918 – 1988) had mild polio as a child. Following an accident whilst driving an ambulance in the Second World

War, the treatment she received for her injured legs was inadequate. As a consequence she relied on a wheelchair for the rest of her life. Felicity Lane-Fox developed respiratory problems and came under the care of Dr Geoffrey Spencer, an anaesthetist with a special interest in intensive care and ventilation and founder of Mead. She was appalled at the condition of the old South Western Hospital unit. Felicity Lane-Fox , a formidable Conservative, and another patient Roy Tearse, a fervent Communist, worked together to raise £1.2m to build a new unit at St Thomas'. Sadly she died just before it opened. She was made a life peer in 1981.

(1989 – open in 2008)

LANSDELL

Lansdell was named after Mary Lansdell (born 1938), Director of Midwifery and midwife teacher at St Thomas'. She trained as a nurse at King's College Hospital and as a midwife in Cardiff and in the London district. She was appointed to the staff of the General Lying-In Hospital which became part of the St Thomas' group. She was appointed Director of Midwifery in 1976, a post she held until her retirement in 1993. Mary Lansdell helped with the planning of the Lansdell Suite for Private Patients which she opened in September 1992. Mrs Mary Wrigley (née Lansdell) is a current member of the Nightingale Fellowship.

(1992 – open in 2008)

LAZARUS

Lazarus was the name of two well known men in the Bible. One was the Lazarus whom Jesus raised from the dead. The other was a hungry beggar who was offered nothing by a rich man who was feasting. After death Lazarus (the beggar) was rewarded but the rich man was punished. The symbolic message was always help others when given the opportunity. **(1576 – 1862)**

LEOPOLD

Leopold (1853 – 1884) was the eighth child of Queen Victoria and Prince Albert. He inherited haemophilia and was frequently in poor health. In 1872 he went to Oxford University and was awarded an honorary doctorate. It is said that he contemplated

Alicia Lloyd Still

marriage to Alice Liddell, the inspiration for Alice in Wonderland. He married Princess Helena Frederica of Waldeck Pyemont with whom he had two children. **(1871 – 1934)**

LILIAN

Lilian was named after Lilian Holland Holland. Both she and her father, Stephen Holland, a Hospital Governor, gave a donation to purchase the Doulton nursery rhyme tiles for the ward. Some of these tiles are now on display along the ground floor corridor. **(1901 – 2005)**

LLOYD STILL

The ward was named after Alicia Lloyd Still (1869 – 1944). She trained in the Nightingale School, was a Staff Nurse in the 1890s and Matron and Superintendent of St Thomas' from 1913 to 1937. Alicia Lloyd Still sat on the first General Nursing Council and was the first President of the Association of Hospital Matrons.

She received numerous other national and international awards and was made a Dame of the British Empire in 1934.

The phrase "consider patients as honoured guests" is attributed to Dame Alicia.

She and Miss Gullan created the post of Sister Tutor and devised the three-year nurse training programme. Between them they also introduced the Nightingale badge and Fellowship and the idea of purpose-built training rooms. Prior to that training had taken place in the nurses' dining room. **(1966 – open in 2008)**

LOUISE

The ward is probably named after Sister Louise, a senior nurse who specialised in dietetics and was also in charge of the domestic staff in the early 1900s. "Sister Louise" became a job title until the introduction of the role of Domestic Superintendent in the 1930s. Louise was chosen as the name of the new metabolic and endocrine unit due to the relevance of diet to this specialty. **(1976 – 1988)**

LUKE

Luke was named after the biblical Apostle and Evangelist whose symbol is the winged ox. Sinning was often held as the reason for suffering and Luke offered hope to the sick poor. He was a physician and is the Patron Saint of physicians. **(1565 – open in 2008)**

LYDIA

In the Bible story Lydia offered hospitality to the Apostles Paul and Barnabas and was one of Paul's earliest converts. She was devout and, when the name was first used, was a symbolic example to the sick poor. **(circa 1576 – in use in 2008 as the name of an outpatients' clinic)**

MAGDALEN

Magdalen was one of the six Great Wards. In the Bible story Mary of Magdala witnessed the crucifixion of Jesus Christ, prepared His body for burial and found His tomb empty. She told the apostles and became known as the apostle to the apostles.
(1576 – 1873; reopened briefly in 1896)

MAKINS

Makins was named after George Makins (1853 – 1933). He was a surgeon at St Thomas' who served in both the Boer and First World Wars. Makins was knighted and appointed President of the Royal College of Surgeons of England from 1917 to 1919. **(Hydestile Hospital)**

MARION OLIVE HAYDON

See Haydon

MARK

Mark was named after the closure of St Mark ward at the South Western Hospital which had been part of the St Thomas' group. The ward was named after St Mark, whose symbol is the lion, and who, it is thought, wrote the

biblical Gospel of St Mark. He is said to have performed many miracles. His head is in Alexandria where he had been murdered but his relics are in St Mark's Basilica, Venice. **(1988 or 1989 – open in 2008)**

MARY

Mary was named after Queen Mary II (1662 – 1694), wife of King William III. She was the elder daughter of Catholic convert King James II. She, however, remained staunchly Protestant and, with her husband, deposed James in the Glorious Revolution of 1688. They reigned jointly from 1689 until she died from smallpox. The Act of Settlement, passed in 1701, was created to ensure that from their reign onwards, only Protestants could succeed to the throne. **(1708 – 2000)**

MEAD

Richard Mead (1673 – 1754) was the son of a Puritan Pastor and so could not enter an English university. Educated in Utrecht, Leyden and Padua, he returned to London in 1696. He was a physician at St Thomas' Hospital from 1703 until 1715. He was a renowned

teacher and believed that students learned best from treating patients. He wrote many books and contributed to many others, on such subjects as poisons, pharmacology and public health. Mead was a philanthropist who encouraged his wealthy patients to support St Thomas'. **(1966 – 1988)**

MITCHINER

Philip Mitchiner (1888 – 1952) was a student at St Thomas' from 1907. He served in the First World War and then continued to work for the Serbian Relief Fund until returning to St Thomas' in 1926. Mitchiner achieved national recognition as an examiner for, and Vice-President of, the Royal College of Surgeons of England. **(1976 – open in 2008)**

NAPLE'S OR NAPLES

The origin of this name has not been discovered. It could have been the name of a benefactor. A century later a gravedigger who became a grave robber (a Resurrectionist) and supplied bodies to Sir Astley Cooper was named Joseph Naples. It has not been possible to make a connection between this later Naples and the ward name introduced a century earlier. **(1717 – 1862)**

NEW

New was used for only a short period. **(1632)**

NIGHTINGALE

Nightingale ward was probably named after Florence Nightingale (1820 – 1910). "Nightingales" were nurses who trained in the School at St Thomas'. In 1860, training involved one year of academic and practical work. There was no examination at the end and no certificate was awarded. By 1925

there was a three-year national curriculum and "Nightingales" were awarded a badge after their fourth year.
(Hydestile 1941 – 1968; STH 1976 – open in 2008)

Deceased nurses' badges are displayed in Central Hall.

NIGHTLAYERS/NIGHTLODGERS

This was one of the six Great Wards. The beds were for poor travellers. In 1602 the ward was renamed Tobias and only the sick poor were admitted. **(1552 – 1602)**

NOAH'S ARK

Noah's Ark was one of the six Great Wards. It was on the upper storey and possibly, the ward with its gabled roof, looked like the vessel which survived the flood in the Old Testament story. In the 1701 rebuilt Hospital, the name became Noah. **(1576 – circa mid-1700s)**

NORTHUMBERLAND

Northumberland came with the Dreadnought

Hospital which, in 1986, moved into St Thomas'. The ward had been named after the 4th Duke (1792 – 1865), a naval officer, philanthropist, and, briefly, First Lord of the Admiralty. In 1872, the fifth Duke gave a generous donation to name the ward in memory of his uncle. **(1986 – open in 2008)**

NUFFIELD

William Morris (1877 – 1963) earned his living repairing bicycles when aged 17. By 1912 he had built the first Morris car factory in Cowley. He became a Baronet in 1929, a Baron in 1934 and a Viscount in 1938. As Lord Nuffield he was a famous philanthropist who, from 1926 until his death, made donations to St Thomas'. **(1934 – 1976)**

OLIVE HAYDON

See Haydon

OPHTHALMIC

Ophthalmic means relating to eyes. Advances in eye surgery during the 1860s led to the setting up of a specialist ward in the new St Thomas' in Lambeth. **(1871 – 1976)**

PAGE

Max Page (1882 – 1963) qualified at St Thomas' in 1906 and was on the surgical staff from 1919 to 1946. Page was highly skilled in orthopaedic, paediatric and general surgery. During the Second World War he was Sector Officer in charge of emergency services at St Thomas'. **(1976 – open in 2008)**

PERKINS

See George Perkins

QUEEN'S

Queen's was one of the Great Wards and is thought to have been named after Mary Tudor (1516 – 1558), the Catholic elder daughter of Henry VIII. She reigned from Edward VI's death in 1553 until 1558. **(circa 1553 – 1862)**

REGENCY

Regency was opened for soldiers injured in the last Napoleonic Campaign. From 1810

George III was too ill to rule and, until his death in 1820, George's eldest son ruled as Prince Regent. The decade was called the Regency. (1817 – 1820)

ROBERT WILLAN

Robert Willan (1757 – 1812) qualified in Edinburgh in 1780 and was the originator of dermatology as a specialty. In 1783 he moved to the Carey Street Public Dispensary in London, where he stayed until 1803. In 1790, Willan published "A Remarkable Case of Abstinence", an early account of a male eating disorder. Willan's 1808 book, "On Cutaneous Diseases", describes the history of dermatology with outstanding illustrations. Willan and his assistant Thomas Bateman worked together on the classification of skin diseases.
(mid 1980s – 2005)

ROYAL EYE

The Surrey Ophthalmic Hospital opened in Lambeth in 1857. It was renamed the Royal Ophthalmic in 1869 when the Princess Royal became Patron. Despite the proximity of Ophthalmic at St Thomas', a new Royal Eye Hospital was opened in 1892. The Hospital was badly damaged by bombs in 1941 so moved into a house in Surbiton. Post-war it moved into Lambeth Hospital before returning to its original site. In 1976 the Royal Eye was integrated into St Thomas'.
(1976 – 2000; outpatients clinic in 2008)

ST THOMAS' HOME

In 1878 the Governors decided to refurbish Adelaide and Alice to accommodate paying patients. The Home opened in 1881. When Gassiot House nurses' home was completed in 1906, St Thomas' Home moved into the ground and first floors. The building was badly damaged in the Second World War.
(1881 – 1940)

SANDS

The Stillbirth and Neonatal Death Society (SANDS) was founded in 1975 to support parents before and after the birth and death of their infant. For more information please go to their website, www.uk-sands.org.
(2003 – open in 2008)

SARAH SWIFT

A portrait of Sarah Swift (1854 – 1937) hangs in the ward named after her. Sarah Swift was Matron of Guy's Hospital from 1900 to 1909. She worked with others to open the College of Nursing in 1916, which by 1921 had become the Royal College of Nursing. Sarah Swift was, during her career, Matron in Chief of the Royal Naval Service, the British Red Cross Society and the Order of St John of Jerusalem in England. She was made a Dame of the British Empire (DBE). In 1999 Naaman and Esther were closed at Guy's and the patients were moved to St Thomas'. The current ward Sister chose to name the new ward Sarah Swift. **(1999 – open in 2008)**

SCUTARI

Scutari was opened in a basement bed store-room after the Hospital was bomb-damaged in the Second World War. The primitive facilities were likened to those experienced by Florence Nightingale and her nurses at the Barrack Hospital, Scutari, during the Crimean War (1854 – 1856). **(1940 – open in 2008)**

Barrack Hospital, Scutari: Florence Nightingale visiting the wards.

SEYMOUR

Seymour was named in memory of Seymour Graves Toller (1867 – 1902) a multiple Gold Medal award winner and assistant physician at St Thomas' Hospital. Due to poor health, Toller went to work in Egypt. He died of tuberculosis in 1902 while Professor of Medicine in Cairo. His grieving fiancée, Lillian Jewesbury, gave a large donation in his memory which financed the purchase of the nursery rhyme Doulton tiles which covered the walls. Some of the tiles have been re-hung along the main corridor at St Thomas'. **(1903 – 2005)**

SIMON

John Simon (1819 – 1904) lectured in pathology for many years until, in 1853, he was appointed as a surgeon at St Thomas'. In 1848, he was the first Medical Officer of Health for the City of London. He was President of the Royal College of Surgeons of England in 1878 and was knighted in 1887. Simon was popular and respected for his important contribution to public health and sanitation. **(1966 – 1994)**

SIMON HOTEL

Simon Hotel is a patient facility. It has 24 bedrooms and is fully serviced. Since 1997 it has been located in Gassiot House.
(1994 – open in 2008)

SOMERSET

Somerset was a ward in the Dreadnought and probably commemorates the twelfth Duke, who was First Lord of the Admiralty from 1859 until 1866. He was interested in naval welfare reform and, due to his efforts, the Greenwich Naval Infirmary became a hospital for the benefit of merchant seafarers. **(1986 – 2004)**

STANLEY

Arthur Stanley (1869 – 1947) was Treasurer at St Thomas' Hospital from 1917 until 1943. He was awarded many honours and was MP for Ormskirk from 1898 until 1918.
(Hydestile Hospital until 1976; 1976 – 2004)

STEPHEN

Stephen was first mentioned in the Guy's Reports of 1853 but there is no record as to why the Governors chose the name. In the

1980s the ward was open at Guy's. In 1997 when the cardiac units were amalgamated at St Thomas' the staff chose to name their ward Stephen. (1997 – open in 2008)

STILL

See Lloyd Still

SUSANNAH

The Bible story of Susannah is in the Book of Daniel. She was a virtuous woman accused of adultery and condemned to death. However the accusation was proved false and her accusers were executed for their lying. This name had symbolic meaning for the sick poor. (1576 – 1782)

SWEAT

Sweat describes the treatment in the wards. Patients with venereal diseases and smallpox were smeared in mercurial ointment, wrapped in flannel and left to sweat. The sweat wards were Job, Judith, Lazarus and Susanna. (1576 – circa 1790s)

SWIFT

See Sarah Swift

THOMAS BATEMAN

Thomas Bateman (1778 – 1821) trained in Edinburgh and moved to London and worked with Robert Willan. When Willan died in 1812, Bateman continued their influential work on skin diseases. In 1813, Bateman published the Practical Synopsis of Cutaneous Disease and, in 1817, the Delineations of Cutaneous Disease. Bateman named many dermatological diseases. One such was Molluscum contagiosum previously known as Bateman's Disease. (mid 1980s – 1995)

TOBIAS

In the Bible story Tobias was sent by his blind father to claim money owed to him. Trusting the help of a stranger Tobias gained the money and a wife by overcoming the demon Ashmodeus. Tobias discovered that the stranger was the angel Raphael who restored the father's sight. The family had trust which was probably the symbolism of the ward name. (1602 – approx mid-1700s)

VICTORIA

Victoria was named after Queen Victoria

(1819 – 1901). Her father was the fourth son of George III but none of her cousins survived infancy. Victoria became queen in 1837, the last monarch of the House of Hanover. In 1840, she married her cousin, Albert of Saxe Coburg-Gotha. They had nine children, who married into many European royal families. Victoria was never out of mourning after Albert's premature death in 1861.

(1871 – 1940s; 1998 – open in 2008)

1

WARDROPER

Wardroper was named after Mrs Sarah Wardroper (1813 – 1892), Matron of St Thomas' from 1854, the year she was widowed, until 1887.

Mrs Wardroper was dedicated to the nursing of the sick poor and was a woman with extraordinary administrative skills.

In 1860 she was chosen by Florence Nightingale to run the Nightingale Training School for Nurses and, at the same time, was responsible for all nurses and patients at St

1 Statue of Queen Victoria, Central Hall
2 Mrs Sarah Wardroper

Thomas'. Between June and September 1862, she managed the temporary move to Surrey Gardens and, in 1871, the permanent move to Lambeth. There the appointment of a Home Sister eased her workload. She helped train nearly 500 "Nightingales" who went to train others worldwide. **(1966 – 1998)**

WESTMINSTER UNIT

Westminster Unit was the name of the private patients' unit at St Thomas'. Gullan, Howard and Mitchiner wards were all part of the unit but by 2008 only Howard remained. The name is appropriate as St Thomas' entrance is on Westminster Bridge Road, and the unit is across the River Thames from the Palace of Westminster. **(1976 – open in 2008)**

WILLAN

See Robert Willan

WILLIAM

William was named after William III (1650 – 1702) the Dutch Protestant William of Orange who in 1677 married Mary, the Protestant elder daughter of James II. In 1688, with popular support, William and Mary became joint monarchs, in the "Glorious Revolution", which ended the Catholic monarchy in England. Mary died in 1694. In 1701, William ensured that only Protestants could ascend the throne of England when Parliament passed the 'Act of Settlement'.
(1735 – 1989)

WILLIAM GULL

see Guy's list **(1999 – open in 2008)**

WRIGLEY

Arthur Joseph (Joe) Wrigley (1902 – 1984), was an obstetrician who trained at St Thomas', qualifying in 1924. He joined the obstetric staff in 1934, becoming head of department in 1946. He received a CBE a few months prior to his retirement in 1965. An eminent teacher and an advisor to the Department of Health, he was the author of a renowned textbook, Gynaecology and Obstetrics and inventor of the "short forceps" that bear his name. In 1958, Wrigley wrote a biography of his colleague Kenneth Bowes.
(1976 – 1980s)

Christmas on the ward c. 1900

GUY'S – "AN HOSPITAL FOR INCURABLES"

THOMAS GUY AND THE FOUNDING OF THE HOSPITAL

Thomas Guy was born in London in 1644 or 1645. The exact date is unknown because, as his parents were Baptists, there is no record in the parish register. His father worked as a lighterman and collier but died in 1652/3. Anne, his mother, took the family back to her home town of Tamworth and gave her children a good education. As his father had been a City of London liveryman Thomas Guy was able to become an apprentice. In 1660 he started work at a bookbinder and book-seller in Cheapside, London. By 1673, he was a Freeman of the City of London and a Stationers' Company liveryman.

Guy was an astute businessman. His first business venture was importing cheap English-language Bibles from Holland as he believed that everyone should be able to read the Bible. He sold these from a shop he had bought in a prime location near the Mansion House in the heart of the City of London, and his profits were high. This venture was not

THE HOLY
BIBLE,
Containing
The Old Testament
AND
THE NEW:

Newly translated out of the
ORIGINAL TONGUES,

And with the former Translations
diligently Compared and Revised
by his MAJESTIES
special Command.

Appointed to be read in Churches.

Printed at the Theater in Oxford, and are
to be sold by Thomas Guy at the Oxford-
Arms on this west side of the Royal-Ex-
change in Cornhill. LONDON, 1685.

entirely legal and brought him into conflict with the Stationers' Company. By joining with Oxford University Press his publishing became legal but the Stationers never really forgave him. Despite his fortune and good deeds, he was never elected Master of the livery company.

In contemporary cartoons Thomas Guy was sometimes depicted as a miser. However, in reality, he was always generous to both the poor and his friends.

From 1677 he gave funds to benefit the citizens of Tamworth, paying for a schoolroom, almshouses, a library and spinning shed. From

1695 until 1701 he represented Tamworth in Parliament and paid for a new Town Hall in 1700. However, when he was not reselected to represent the town in 1707, his anger was overwhelming. He gave no further funds to Tamworth.

Guy lived a frugal life. He disliked ceremony, declining the post of Sheriff of London for which he was fined £420. However, in 1704 he did accept the invitation to become a Governor of St Thomas' Hospital which enabled him to add "Esquire" to his name. In 1707 Guy made a donation of £1,000 which funded the building of a new female ward block at the Hospital. Fourteen years later he was sufficiently wealthy to build an entire hospital costing £18,793-16s-1d and set up an endowment to fund its future income.

As a Governor, Guy became aware that often patients who were discharged from Hospital were unfit to return to work. They needed a period of convalescence.

In 1720, Guy made a profit of over £200,000 from the timely sale of South Sea Stock. He now had sufficient funds to realise his dream and build Mr Guy's Hospital for Incurables.

Thomas Guy caricatured as a miser

1

subsequently been made a "Saint" on at least two occasions. In 1758 a burial register records a death in Saint Guy's and in 2007 an event at Saint Guy's was promoted by a local newspaper!

A DREAM REALISED

In the 18th and 19th centuries, it was the duty of women to care for the sick in the home. There were charitable hospitals like St Thomas' which offered free medical treatment to the poor. However, these did not provide care for the chronically sick or mentally ill, at that time described as incurables and lunatics respectively.

Guy intended that his hospital would have a complementary function to St Thomas'. Patients "passing out" from St Thomas' would be admitted to Guy's until fit enough to look after themselves.

In 1721 work started on Guy's Hospital on land leased from St Thomas' for 999 years. Guy died four months before his hospital was completed. In his Will, he left sufficient funds to complete the building works, to create an endowment fund so that the new hospital had an income, and to commission a statue in his memory. The present-day chapel was not built for nearly 50 years. In 1774 Thomas Guy Esquire was laid to rest in its crypt. He has

1 Thomas Guy discussing the plans for his hospital with Dr Mead, the physician, and Mr Steat, the architect who designed the East Wing.
  Painting by C W Cope, R.A. 1877
2 Guy's Hospital Crest: 'Dare Quam Accipere - *to give is better than to receive*'
3 Guy's Hospital for Incurables, 1725. Engraving by Thomas Bowles
4 Statue of Thomas Guy by Peter Scheemakers, erected in 1739

3

Although appointed after his death the first Court of Committees (Governors), President, Treasurer, Steward, Apothecary and Matron were all known to Thomas Guy. They appointed medical staff whom they believed shared their commitment to implementing the wishes of Guy for his Hospital. Gradually, over the next 50 years, land was acquired and cleared for the building of the Front Court with its East and West Wings. Scheemakers' statue of Thomas Guy was erected in 1739 in the Front Court where it stands today, as do the 1725 buildings although these are considerably altered internally.

The Hospital entrance was from Collingwood Street. Originally entirely colonnaded at ground floor level there is today only a central colonnade running north to south. These colonnades were a link with the monastic infirmaries of past centuries. The wards had large windows for ventilation and were situated on the first, second and third floors. There were open fires for heating, candle-holders for lighting, a water supply from a reservoir tank on the roof and a brewery.

Patients were not admitted immediately. Confusion about the date and sequence of events arose because, in 1752, the British calendar was revised and started in January rather than April. For simplicity this text will use 1 January 1725 as New Year. Matron was appointed in May. In October, the Court of Committees Ordered: "That the Several Wards of this Hospital be named as now by Mr Treasurer's proposed list: **Job, Lazarus, Luke, Naaman, Samaritan, Charity, Dorcas, Lydia,**

Martha and **Patience** and it is further ordered that the Names be affixed to the Respective Wards as the Treasurer shall direct." A total of 60 beds is mentioned. In December 1725 **Cross** is named as the ward for fluxing patients. Fluxing was the administration of liquids believed to cleanse the body.

The Hospital was extended in 1745, with the addition of the East Wing. The West Wing, completed in 1774, included the elegant Chapel and Matron's House, both of which are in use today.

A Chapel had previously been sited above the central colonnade. The space created by its move became **Chapel** ward. The name was subsequently changed to **Esther**. In 1788 two more wards were created by infilling colonnades. **Accident,** was soon renamed **Astley Cooper** and then **Dorcas**. **Cornelius**, a medical ward, did not open until 1808.

THE NINETEENTH CENTURY

Guy's Medical School was established in 1825. This was largely due to the efforts of the eminent Guy's clinicians Astley Cooper, Richard Bright and William Gull.

Other notable staff of the early 19th century are the father and son apothecaries, both named William Stocker, and Joseph Towne, whose world - renowned wax models in the **Gordon Museum** are still used for teaching anatomy. Perhaps most importantly for the Hospital's survival was the arrival of **Benjamin Harrison**. He was appointed a Governor when aged 21, and five years later succeeded as Treasurer his father who died in 1797, the same year that he had opened the Lunatic House.

Harrison was aware that discipline was lax. Patients broke even the most basic rules regarding "restraint from spitting about the wards and other instances of un-cleanliness which offend decency". He also disliked the

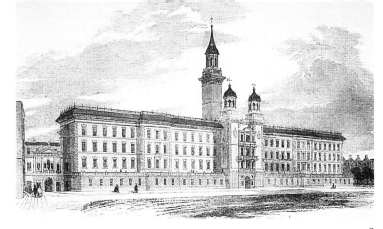

2

narrow, overcrowded and unsanitary streets on three sides of the Hospital. They were a potential source of fire and disease. He persuaded the Governors to purchase nearby land as it became available in the hope of receiving funds to pay for new buildings. In 1829 came the welcome and extraordinary bequest of Sir William Hunt, a Guy's Governor and friend of Harrison. Hunt bequeathed £180,000 to Guy's stipulating that it should be spent within three years on enlarging the Hospital to create an extra 100 beds. Hunt's request to be buried beside Thomas Guy, in the crypt of Guy's Chapel, with no inscription, was met.

Harrison immediately purchased many properties in Sutton Street and opened **Petersham** (27 beds for women and warm baths), a new **Lunatic House** (24 beds), 11-bedded **Ruth**, for female eye patients, and **Billet** ward for 10 patients "infested with vermin or in a frenzied state", with a bake-house for baking their dirty linen. A warehouse became the temporary **Hunt's House**, with a total of 101 beds in two men's wards possibly named **Stephen** and **Philip**. Another converted house was opened as the **Eye Infirmary** (30 beds) which included **Barnabas** (**Barnaby**) but which also admitted women with uterine problems. From 1831, women were admitted for lying-in (childbirth) into an adjacent house named **Mary**. Another house, already named Miriam, became **Miriam** (18 beds) and the first specialist children's out-patient clinic also had beds – but its location and name are not recorded.

The Weston Street Estate was probably acquired in 1828 and Guy's occupied over twice the ground first earmarked in the 1720s. In 1851 the estate was cleared for the construction of **Hunt's House**. The South Wing was occupied from 1852, although the North Wing was not completed until 1871 – the same year as the new St Thomas' Hospital was opened in Lambeth. The total cost of Hunt's

1 The Middle Colonnade from an engraving by Thomas Bowles, 1725
2 Sketch of Hunt's House 1870s

House was under £67,000, just over one-third of the £180,000 Hunt left in his will.

When Guy's new wards opened they were dedicated to patients with medical conditions. All surgical patients were cared for in the original buildings, Guy's House. When Hunt's House was completed the Hospital could accommodate a total of 523 patients.

The Reports show that three temporary wards, **Talbot**, **Spare** and **Extra** were on the ground floor of the South Wing. These were closed when the Wing fully opened in 1853. The wards were then **Stephen**, **Philip**, **Job**, **Lazarus** and **Naaman** for men and **Martha**, **Lydia** and **Charity** for women.

When the North Wing was built the basement kitchens were connected underground to the South Wing and Guy's House. These subways are in use today.

The North Wing contained the Eye Infirmary and eye wards **Barnabas** and **Ruth**, the anatomical museum and wards, of which only three are recorded: **Addison**, **Bright** and **Astley Cooper**.

Formal, residential nurse training started at Guy's Hospital in 1879 although the School of Nursing was not opened until 1907.

The nurses' accommodation was on the top floor of Hunt's House but with its poor ventilation, excessive light for staff needing to sleep during the day and the presence of rats and other vermin, it was not a pleasant environment. Conditions greatly improved for the nurses with the opening of the purpose-built **Henrietta Raphael** Nurses' Home in 1901.

1 Henrietta Raphael Nurses' Home kitchen
2 Nurses off duty

Hunt's House was not the only sign of Guy's continuing growth during the 19th century. In the early 1860s Lunatic was converted into the **Clinical** wards **John** and **Miriam**, the School of Midwifery opened in 1884, the Dental School in 1888 and the Medical School College in 1890, but generally the Governors found funds were insufficient. They introduced changes in administration and, from 1884, charged patients for admission into the refurbished **Bright**. However, by the end of the century the Hospital was in severe financial difficulty and some wards were closed. A new Treasurer solved these financial problems.

PEACE AND WAR 1900 – 1945

Sir Henry Cosmo Orme Bonsor was appointed Treasurer in 1896 and President of Guy's Hospital in 1910. Within two years of becoming Treasurer, he had established an endowment fund, persuaded the Prince of Wales to be its President and raised £200,000.

Despite the 1899 to 1902 Boer War, commem-

orated by a small wall fountain in Guy's House east quadrangle, public donations ensured that the fund grew. In 1900 basement rooms in Guy's House were adapted for use as children's wards. In 1901 an internal telephone system was installed and new operating theatres were built above the central colonnade of Guy's House. In 1908 a Social Work department was opened and the following year a new Casualty department.

Due to Bonsor's efforts Guy's joined St Thomas' as one of London's leading hospitals, attracting staff of the highest calibre.

The main impact of World War I was the depletion of staff for military service. **Stephen** was reserved for wounded officers.

In the Court of Governors Report for December 1918 there is a list of monies donated through the ward collection boxes naming **Addison**, **Astley Cooper**, **Bright**, **Charity**, **Clinical**, **Cornelius**, **Dorcas**, **Esther**, **Evelyn**, **Eye**, **Job**, **Lazarus**, **Luke**, **Lydia**, **Martha**, **Mary**, **Naaman**,

Patience, **Queen**, and **Officers Section (Stephen)**. Of these, **Evelyn** and **Queen** were new but there is no indication of their location.

After the war Guy's was again short of funds. Fortunately appeals were supported. Leopold Salomons gave money for the 1920 outpatient Salomon's Centre for Infant Welfare, in Newcomen Street. Three years later the **New Children's Ward**, donated by the Bermondsey and Rotherhithe War Memorial Committee, opened in an adjacent enclosed colonnade.

Sir Percy Shepherd was another benefactor. In 1921 **Shepherd House** opened with accommodation for nurses and the physiotherapy school.

Two more donations were received before the Second World War. Lord Nuffield financed the Private Patients building, **Nuffield House**, which opened in 1935 and a £20,000 legacy financed the opening of **Caleb** and **Diplock**.

Guy's suffered several direct hits from bombs in the Second World War. Hunt's House central staircase was destroyed but amazingly only one person was slightly injured. Beds were needed for people in shock so, with some wards inaccessible, **Hilton** was opened. In December 1940 the basement of Shepherd's House and the subway connections were severely damaged. Fortunately no nurse was injured as all were on the wards for "hand-over".

On 16 April 1941 incendiary (fire) bombs hit Guy's. The Governors' Court Room, the elegant staircase and all the other Front Court East Wing buildings were lost in the flames.

When Tabard House, home to the works department, was bombed Guy's had temporary maintenance difficulties but the Hospital never closed.

2

Supplemented by a donation from Lord Nuffield the York Clinic opened in 1944 with 43 beds, in **Robert Gillespie**, **Maurice Craig**, **George Savage** and **John Dickson** wards. There were also paramedical facilities and recreation rooms. An anonymous donor had given £43,000 as a tribute to the work of Robert Gillespie. It was intended for patients "of moderate means" who were mentally ill but not insane, and the first patients were officers traumatised by warfare.

RECONSTRUCTION 1945 – 1960

When the war ended only six wards with 295 beds were open but repair work was soon started.

Sarah Swift (gynaecology) was a temporary prefabricated ward on the east side of Front Court.

In Guy's House, **Astley Cooper**, **Christopher**, **Dorcas**, **Job**, **Luke**, **Lydia**, **Queen**, **Patience** and **Samaritan**, known affectionately as Pat and Sam, were the nine surgical wards. **Evelyn**, **Keats** and **Naaman** were too badly damaged to accommodate patients.

Hunt's House had a temporary staircase installed. In the South Wing were **Victoria** (maternity) **Bright** and **Wilks** (men) and the children's unit **Caleb** for surgical and **Diplock** for medical conditions. In the North Wing **Barnabas** (men) and **Ruth** (women) admitted patients with neurological, ophthalmic and venereal conditions whilst **Mary** and **Miriam**

1 *A Day at Guy's Hospital* by G Earle Wickham, late 1940s
2 Guy's on fire 1940s

(women), **Addison** and **John** (men) were general wards. **William Gull** (men and women) was a specialist diabetic and endocrine ward.

The Old London Bridge Alcove and the statues of Thomas Guy and Lord Nuffield were undamaged in the war. The War Memorial Arch, between Hunt's House and Guy's House, also survived the bombing. It was removed in 1962 but has been restored, inscribed with names of Guy's men and women who died in both world wars, and now stands on a paved area at the Southern end of The Park close to the **Hodgkin Building**.

During the war Bertie Lees Reed, Clerk to the Governors, had the foresight to acquire bombed, derelict land east of Great Maze Pond, as a site for a new hospital. In the mid-1950s the Department of Health finally gave the Governors permission for a three-stage redevelopment programme.

At that time Guy's House was sinking, as the wooden supports on which it had been built had rotted. High pressure machines pumped cement under all the 1725 buildings to form firm new foundations. A new Governors' Court Room was opened on the ground floor of the east quadrangle. In 1992 this was named the Burfoot Court Room in honour of A H (Harry) Burfoot who had served as Clerk to the Governors for many years.

In the 1960s **Addison** was known as the haunted ward. A bygone sister had accidentally killed a patient and her ghost was said to touch the shoulder of any nurse about to make a similar mistake. After the ward was divided in the 1980s the phantom sister was felt in **Addison** but never in **Hurst**.

Other new ward names at this time reflect medical advances. **Peter Bishop** was an endocrine and diabetic ward, **Starling** an intensive care unit and **Charles Symonds** a ward for elderly patients.

REBUILDING 1960 – 2008

STAGE ONE NEW GUY'S HOUSE

In 2008 the building was divided into three areas: Borough Wing, Minor Injuries, and Tabard Annex.

New Guy's House was designed as a self-contained, 10-storey building for surgical patients. Whilst digging the foundations, a Roman barge was discovered and following examination was left where it had been found. Archeologists believed that Guy's was built on the site of a Roman dockyard.

When, in 1990, further excavations uncovered a Roman waterfront perfectly preserved in the thick, wet mud, Guy's became an official (buried) archaeological site.

2

The first patients were admitted in 1961. Despite the wealth of other information available on the building, the names of the wards were not recorded. They were located on the third to ninth floors and all 378 beds had a modern bedside control panel. Through personal communications it has been possible to establish that the original ward names were **Lydia** and **Cornelius**, **Job** (thoracic), **Luke**, **Astley Cooper** (men's general), **Martha**, **Sarah** (women's general), **Dorcas** (cardiothoracic), **Evelyn** (general), **Christopher**, **Queen** (orthopaedic), **Patience** and **Samaritan** (both general and still known as Pat and Sam), **Esther** and **Naaman** (both general).

Benefactors were appreciated. One ward was named **Christopher** in accordance with the wishes of the staff of the Bank of England who had raised over £30,000.

There were many changes in ward use and names in New Guy's House after the opening of Guy's Tower in 1974, the 1993 merger with St Thomas' and other events. **Brook** made a brief appearance for elderly patients. The increasing use of day surgery resulted in a reduced need of surgical beds. In the 1980s Esther was a general medical and Naaman a urology ward. When in 1999 urology moved to St Thomas' **Esther** and **Naaman** were refurbished and for two years accommodated women with their new-born babies.

For many years the various combinations of Guy's and St Thomas' caused confusion for staff, patients and visitors. On 7 January 2008 names were changed: the western part of New Guy's House became **Borough Wing**, with **Tabard Annex** (oncology) to the east of the central Minor Injuries Department.

At that time (2008) the following wards were open: **Russell Brock** (post-operative recovery), **Richard Bright** (renal transplant), **Frederick** (home dialysis), **Astley Cooper** (dialysis), **Patience** (surgery), **Hedley Atkins** (breast surgery and general oncology), **Samaritan** (oncology), **Dorcas** (thoracic surgery). The renal outpatient and inpatient unit was **Bostock**.

STAGE TWO GUY'S TOWER

In 2008 renamed Tower Wing.

In 1960 planning started for the tallest hospital building in the world.

Building upwards was essential to produce the required clinical floor area on the relatively small site. The official opening by HM Queen Elizabeth II was on 6 May 1976.

The communications and services component of the Tower was designed to hide the boiler house chimney flues.

The clinical and research component had 30 floors above the ground floor. When the first patients were admitted in 1974 it housed wards for all paediatric and women's services and the dental school. The **McNair Centre** (antenatal outpatients) was on the Ground Floor. On the first floor was **Grant Massie** (post-operative recovery room) which soon became **Cornelius** and later **Russell Brock**. All other wards were on the ninth to the 16th floors.

The Evelina Children's Hospital occupied four floors. The wards were **Caleb** and **Diplock** (burns and isolation), **Dickens** (renal and general), **William Little** later renamed **Ronnie Mac Keith** (medical), **Hector Cameron** (psychiatry), **Rothschild** and **The Borough** (surgery) and **Arthur Farre** (baby unit).

Women's services occupied the next four floors with wards **Victoria**, **Blundell** and **Lever** (obstetric) and **Braxton Hicks** (gynaecology).

Guy's Dental Hospital occupied floors 19 to 28 having two wards: **Patience** and **Sarah**.

In 2008 the only ward open in the Tower Wing was **Blundell** (ENT oncology).

STAGE THREE THOMAS GUY HOUSE

In 2008 divided into two Wings:
Southwark Wing – Atrium 1 and Outpatients
Bermondsey Wing – Atrium 2, Atrium 3, York Clinic, wards and offices.

Thomas Guy House enwraps the lower floors of the Tower, has six floors and is mainly used for outpatient departments. Building started in 1990, but after the July 1991 "Topping Out" there were frequent long delays with construction. The Government dropped its support for Guy's leading to a fiercely fought

"Save Guy's" campaign and the 1993 merger of St Thomas' and Guy's. However work was completed by 1997 and the building was officially opened by HM Queen Elizabeth II on 18 March 1998.

the ward was renamed **John Ruskin**. Other wards are **Job** (elderly), **John Dickson** (men), **Snowsfields Unit** (adolescents) and the **Weston Unit** (learning disability). There are four wards in the Wing which are not accessed from the York clinic. These are two orthopaedic wards **Sarah** (men) and **Queen** (women) and two urological named **Florence** and **Aston Key**.

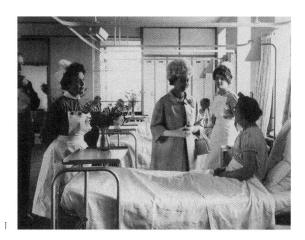

1

The York Clinic, which in 2008 provided mental health services on behalf of South London and Maudsley NHS Foundation Trust, initially had two acute admission wards **John Dickson** and **Maurice Craig**. As psychiatric services altered Maurice Craig became an outpatient unit and

1 HM Queen Elizabeth II opens Thomas Guy House in 1998
2 Guy's Mini Museum in Atrium 1
3 View from Guy's Tower looking west

2

THE FUTURE

In August 1998 the Guy's Hospital site became King's College London's main centre for dental and medical teaching and research. Hunt's House was demolished and New Hunt's House built to house "state of the art" teaching and research facilities.

Thomas Guy could not have envisaged the changes to his hospital in the centuries after his death. In 1725 there were four consultant surgeons, 11 nurses and one pharmacist for 10 wards.

In 2008 one ward alone was visited by four consultant surgeons, 17 nurses and a dedicated pharmacist, physiotherapist and food server. Surely he would be satisfied that his legacy is in safe hands as Guy's continues to offer high quality health services and remains a leader in research and teaching.

THE WARDS
OF GUY'S HOSPITAL

Dates at the end of an entry indicate when the ward name was first used and if the ward is open, or when the name was last used.

ACCIDENT

Accident was named because the patients were emergency admissions. The name was soon changed to Astley Cooper and then Dorcas. **(1788 – early 1780s)**

ADDISON

Thomas Addison (1793 – 1860) qualified at Edinburgh and, in 1815, moved to London where he studied under Thomas Bateman. In 1820 he was appointed assistant physician at Guy's and physician in 1837. Addison

described both pernicious anaemia and a wasting condition due to destruction of the adrenal cortex subsequently named Addison's Disease. **(1871 – 1990s)**

Thomas Addison

ARTHUR FARRE

Arthur Farre (1811 – 1887) studied medicine at Cambridge and St Bartholomew's, qualifying in 1833. Farre was Professor of Obstetric Medicine at King's College London from 1841 to 1862, an examiner for the Royal College of Surgeons of England and physician to Queen Victoria and her family. He was present when, in 1866, Evelina Rothschild died in premature childbirth. Farre influenced Rothschild's decision to build the Evelina Hospital for Sick Children. He assisted in the

Hospital's design and chaired the Management Committee. **(1975 – 2005)**

ASTLEY COOPER

Astley Paston Cooper (1768 – 1841) was apprenticed at Guy's to his uncle William in 1784, and then to Sir Henry Cline at St Thomas'. In 1800 his uncle retired and Astley Cooper was appointed to the staff of Guy's. Cooper was skilled at dissection and an inspirational lecturer. He led the campaign to make bodies available for dissection. He was knighted in 1822 and became President of the Royal College of Surgeons. After his retirement in 1825, he continued dissecting and writing textbooks. In 1833 he received the French Legion of Honour and in 1836 was elected President of the Royal College of Surgeons for a second time. **(early 1800s – open in 2008)**

Astley Paston Cooper

ASTON KEY

Charles Aston Key (1793 – 1849) was apprenticed to his father, also a doctor, in 1810. He became a pupil at Guy's in 1814 and in 1815 apprenticed to Astley Cooper. Aston Key was appointed as a full surgeon at Guy's in 1824, the year he introduced a new technique for lithotomy which established his reputation. He was liked despite his brusque manner and lectured at Guy's Medical School from 1825 to 1844. In 1847 he was appointed surgeon to Prince Albert. Aston Key died of cholera. **(1992 – open in 2008)**

ATKINS

See Hedley Atkins

BARNABAS

Barnabas, the Patron Saint of Cyprus, was an apostle and martyr who journeyed with Paul. An effective preacher, he was seized by his adversaries, tortured and killed. **(1830s – 1974)**

BARNABY

Mentioned in a Guy's Report, this is probably a mis-spelling of Barnabas. **(1830s)**

BILLET

The Crooked Billet public house was bought in 1831 and converted into a ward for "unclean" men. It was demolished when The Park was designed. **(1831 – 1860s)**

BISHOP

See Peter Bishop

BLUNDELL

James Blundell (1790 – 1878) was a pupil at Guy's. In 1818 he was appointed to Guy's and St Thomas' as a lecturer in physiology and midwifery. When the schools split in 1825 Blundell became lecturer in midwifery at Guy's. Although not the first person to perform a blood transfusion (recorded to be a physician unsuccessfully treating Pope Innocent VIII in 1490), from 1818 Blundell did many transfusion experiments and paved the way for routine human transfusion. From 1831 until he resigned in 1834 he was in charge of "diseases of women" at Guy's which included midwifery. Blundell was valued as a clinician and lecturer, amassing a large private practice. He never married and died leaving a £20

million fortune. **(1974 – open in 2008)**

BOROUGH

The name is derived from the Anglo-Saxon word Burgh, a ditch with ramparts which was a defensive fortification. The Burgh built in 910 AD protected the residents of Sudwerca (Southwark) and was probably also their River Thames crossing.

The Evelina Hospital for Sick Children was built in the Borough district of Southwark, making Borough a logical name for a ward when the hospital transferred to Guy's. **(1975 – 2005)**

BOROUGH WING

This was named after the Southwark District. See Borough **(open in 2008)**

BOSTOCK

Bostock was named after John Bostock (1773 – 1846). Bostock's early interest was chemistry which he studied in London but he undertook medical training in Edinburgh, graduating in 1798. Bostock had a successful practice in his home city of Liverpool and, by 1817, was sufficiently wealthy to return to London and specialise in chemistry. In 1822 he was appointed chemistry tutor at Guy's Hospital. His interest in kidney disease resulted in correspondence between him and Bright. These show that it was Bostock who described fundamental concepts still used in renal medicine. **(1990s – open in 2008)**

BRAXTON HICKS

See St Thomas' list **(1974 – 1990s)**

BRIGHT

Richard Bright (1789 – 1858) was born into a wealthy banking family. From 1808 until 1813 he studied medicine in Edinburgh and Guy's and spent the following six years studying in various European centres, including London. In 1820 he became an assistant physician at Guy's. He set up in medical practice, was made a Fellow of the Royal Society and was appointed physician to Guy's in 1824 where he worked for the

next 34 years. His great colleague was Dr Thomas Addison and his invaluable collaborator the chemist Bostock. Bright was renowned as a teacher and for his 1827 work "Reports of Medical Cases". He is known as the "father of nephrology". He described glomerulonephritis, which bears his name, "Bright's Disease". In 1836 he was founding editor of Guy's Hospital Reports. He died suddenly of cardiac disease.

(1871 – open in 2008)

BROCK

See Russell Brock

BROOK

Brook might have been named after the Brook Hospital in Woolwich, built in 1894 to 1896. It was one of 11 fever hospitals around London. During The Second World War the hospital received a direct hit from a V2 rocket but was repaired and remained open until 1995.
(1980s)

Richard Bright

CALEB

Caleb was named after Caleb Diplock (1841 – 1936) a wealthy landowner and philanthropist. After his death his Will gave his Trustees sole discretion to distribute large sums. The Trustees donated £20,000 to Guy's on condition the money was spent on a children's department. Bright was converted into the children's unit with two wards named Caleb and Diplock. **(1936 – 2005)**

CAMERON

See Hector Cameron

CHAPEL

In 1774 Guy's Chapel was completed in Front Court. The old chapel above the central colonnade of Guy's House was converted to a ward. **(1774 – 1785)**

Guy's Chapel

CHARITY

It has been suggested that the famous biblical passage from 1 Corinthians 13:1, which ends "…but the greatest of these is Charity" explains the name. Guy's Hospital relied on charitable donations and the sick poor relied on kindly attention. **(1725 – 1918)**

CHARLES SYMONDS

Charles Putnam Symonds (1890 – 1978), the son of Guy's surgeon Sir Charters Symonds, was educated at Rugby, New College Oxford and Guy's. Qualifying in 1915, he served in France during the First World War. After recovering from war wounds Symonds trained at The National Hospital for Nervous Diseases, London, and was appointed as the first full-time neurologist at Guy's in 1920.

Symonds was interested in psychoneuroses and during the Second World War worked with RAF bomber crews suffering from stress. He was knighted in 1946. He was internationally

recognised as a neurologist and teacher. He retired from Guy's in 1955.
(1970s – 1990s)

CHRISTOPHER

Christopher was named after St Christopher (the carrier of Christ) at the request of the staff of the Bank of England. Between 1919 and 1944 they raised over £30,000 to endow initially a bed and then the ward as a tribute to their First World War fallen colleagues.
(1925 – 1970s or 1980s)

CLINICAL

Clinical was the name of two wards, connected by a small discussion room where patients who were helpful for teaching purposes were accommodated.
(1830s – 1919)

COOPER

See Astley Cooper

CORNELIUS

In the biblical story, Cornelius was a devout man of Caesarea. Peter travelled to Caesarea and preached to Cornelius and his friends. They believed Peter and were baptised. The name had symbolic significance.
(1788 – 1997)

CRAIG

See Maurice Craig

CROSS

It is not known why this name was chosen. Perhaps the ward was cross-shaped. The name is recorded twice in the Court of Committees' Reports. **(1726)**

DICKENS

Charles Dickens (1812 – 1870) was born in Portsmouth. His education ended in 1821 when his father was imprisoned in Marshalsea, Borough, for debt, along with Charles' mother and siblings. Charles was sent to work in a blacking factory but lived close to the prison in Lant Street. He returned to school when his father

Mr. Charles Dickens' Last Reading,
Illustrated London News 1870

was released. In 1833 he became a parliamentary reporter and his sketches were published under the pseudonym Boz. In 1836 he married the daughter of his editor and in the same year his first novel, "The Pickwick Papers", was published in serial form. His books described the miserable living and working conditions of his childhood, and drew attention to social injustice. He was energetic, a charismatic speaker and travelled in the UK, Europe and the USA. Dickens left his wife and 10 children in 1858. He died of a stroke and is buried in Westminster Abbey. **(1975 – 2005)**

DICKSON

See John Dickson

DIPLOCK

See Caleb

DORCAS

See St Thomas' List **(1725 – open in 2008)**

ESTHER

The biblical story of Esther and her heroic deeds is told in the Book of Esther. She had faith, courage and concern for others. These were qualities to admire and emulate. **(1780s – 1999)**

EVELINA

See Evelina Hospital for Sick Children list.

EVELYN

The reason for the choice of name could not be discovered. A possibility is that Evelyn was requested by a benefactor. **(1914 – listed in 1973)**

EXTRA

The name is listed in the Governors' Reports as temporary accommodation. **(1852)**

EYE INFIRMARY

The Eye Infirmary had two wards, Barnabas and Ruth. **(1828 – 1974)**

FARRE

See Arthur Farre

FLORENCE

See St Thomas' list. **(1999 – open in 2008)**

FREDERICK

Frederick Akbar Mohamed (1849 – 1884), whose paternal grandfather was from Patna, India was born and educated in Sussex. He entered Guy's in 1869 and won many prizes whilst training. He married soon after qualifying in 1872 and took medical officer posts elsewhere to support his family. Mohamed returned to Guy's as an assistant physician in 1881. He had extraordinary energy and enthusiasm and in his short life initiated the Collective Investigation Record (which led to collaborative clinical trials), research on the causes of high blood pressure and its relationship to renal disease, surgery for appendicitis and the continuation of Blundell's research on blood transfusion. He died of typhoid fever. **(New in 2008)**

GEORGE SAVAGE

George Henry Savage (1842 – 1921) entered Guy's medical school in 1861 and in 1874, when John Dickson retired, became Lecturer in Mental Health.

Savage, an intrepid mountaineer, climbed the Matterhorn in 1879.

He founded a mental health journal and published many articles. In 1896 he was the first physician for mental diseases at Guy's but could only give opinions as he had no clinics and no beds. Savage was witty, with a great intellect, and popular as an after-dinner speaker. He and Maurice Craig were renowned for having treated Virginia Woolf. Savage received a Knighthood. He retired in 1903. **(1944 – 1997)**

GILLESPIE

See Robert Gillespie

GRANT MASSIE

Grant Massie (1896 – 1964) qualified at Guy's in 1920. He was appointed senior anatomy demonstrator, surgical registrar and, in 1927, clinical tutor in surgery. In 1928 he wrote a popular textbook on surgical anatomy and was appointed surgeon four years later. Massie served in India during the Second World War and was awarded a CBE in 1944. He returned to Guy's and also worked at

Bromley and Putney Hospitals. After retiring he served as a Governor of Guy's. **(1974)**

GULL

See William Gull

HECTOR CAMERON

Hector Charles Cameron (1878 – 1958), went to Cambridge and trained at Guy's where he was known as Charles. In 1911 he became an assistant physician and from 1912 until 1915 was Dean of the medical school. His interest was child health in which he worked from 1920 until 1945. He had great integrity and ability as a teacher and communicator. His main hobby was writing medical biographies. Cameron's 1954 publication "Mr Guy's Hospital 1726 – 1948" is the most recent account of Guy's history. **(1975 – 2005)**

HEDLEY ATKINS

Hedley Atkins (1905 – 1983) went to Rugby School and Oxford. He trained at Guy's, joined the staff in 1937 and became director of the department of surgery in 1954. In 1934 he was appointed Fellow of the Royal College of

Surgeons of England and from 1966 to 1969 was its President. Although a general surgeon, his special interest was breast surgery and he pioneered advances in this field. The ward has a plaque commemorating the opening of Hedley Atkins ward at New Cross Hospital on 28 October 1975. **(1980s – open in 2008)**

HILTON

John Hilton (1805 – 1878) entered Guy's as a pupil in 1824. He was a demonstrator in anatomy at the age of 24 and a surgeon at Guy's from 1844 until 1870. Hilton was appointed Fellow of the Royal Society in 1839 and performed the elaborate dissections on which Joseph Towne based his famous anatomical wax models, still used as teaching aids today. In 1860 he gave a series of 18 specialist lecturers on "Rest and Pain", being convinced that rest was therapeutic once pain relief had been achieved. In 1871 he was appointed Surgeon Extraordinary to Queen Victoria. His daughter married Charles Fagge and they were the predecessors to three generations of doctors at Guy's and St Thomas'. **(1940)**

HURST

Hurst was named after Sir Arthur Hurst (1879 – 1944). As Arthur Hertz he entered Guy's medical school in 1902. In 1906 he was appointed demonstrator of physiology and a year later, assistant physician. In 1911 Hertz demonstrated that radio-opaque liquids could be used for the diagnosis of and research into conditions of the alimentary tract. During the First World War, Hertz changed his surname. Although a gastroenterologist, Hurst started the first neurology clinic. He also introduced combined rounds and ward discussions and edited the Guy's Hospital Reports. Asthma

forced him to retire in 1939. **(1974 – 1990s)**

JOB

See St Thomas' list. **(1725 – open in 2008)**

JOHN

John was probably named after either John the Baptist or John the Apostle whose symbol was an eagle. **(1860 – 1997)**

JOHN DICKSON

John Thompson Dickson (1843 – 1874) qualified at Guy's in 1867, was appointed lecturer in 1869 and the first lecturer in mental diseases in 1871. Dickson had mitral valve disease as a result of juvenile rheumatic fever but practised medicine and wrote extensively. His special interest was epilepsy and its associated convulsions. Dickson held appointments at two lunatic asylums and his criticism of treatment of the mentally ill created enemies. Contrary to prevailing thought, Dickson believed that some forms of insanity and hysteria were beyond the patient's control. Dickson died suddenly of his heart problem. **(1944 – open in 2008)**

JOHN RUSKIN

John Ruskin (1819 – 1900), was a famous art critic, conservationist, and social reformer. He had no direct connection to Guy's Hospital. Nurses who were based at a psychiatric unit in Camberwell, near Ruskin Park and John Ruskin Street, chose the ward name.
(2002 – open in 2008)

KEATS

John Keats (1795 – 1821) was born near Moorgate, London. He was well educated despite the death of his father in 1804 and his mother in 1810, the year he was apprenticed to an apothecary.

In 1815 Keats was accepted as a pupil at Guy's. It is claimed that while living at 6 St Thomas's Street with his friend Henry Stephens, he penned the immortal phrase "A thing of beauty is a joy for ever".

After only one year Keats left Guy's to concentrate on writing poetry. His first works were published in 1817 and a second set in 1820 the year he went to Rome. He hoped to recover from tuberculosis, from which his brother had died in 1818, but he too died, within three months. On 23 October 2007, a bronze life-size figure of Keats was placed sitting in the Old London Bridge alcove in the east quadrangle of Guy's House.
(1930s – 1940s)

1 John Keats

2 Photograph of Keats' statue © Piers Allardyce for Guy's and St Thomas' Charity

KEY

See Aston Key

LAZARUS

See St Thomas' list. **(1725 – 1961)**

LEVER

Lever was named after John Charles Lever (1811 – 1859). Although very poor, he was accepted as a pupil at Guy's in 1823 and qualified in 1834. He initially worked as a general practitioner but was appointed assistant to the Guy's Lying-in charity in 1842 and, jointly with Henry Oldham, became Guy's first obstetrician. Lever discovered that women suffering with convulsions in pregnancy had albumin in their urine. His popularity as consultant enabled him to enjoy a lavish lifestyle but this led to his premature death. **(1974 – 2002)**

LITTLE

See William John Little

LUKE

See St Thomas' list. **(1725 – 1999)**

LUNATIC HOUSE

Thomas Guy founded his hospital for those who were incurable or insane. Men and women were confined in separate areas and usually restrained with chains. In the mid-1850s the Governors decided that the Hospital was unsuitable for the care of the insane. The house was converted into the Clinical wards. **(1797 – mid-1850s)**

LYDIA

See St Thomas' list. **(1725 – 1997)**

MAC KEITH

See Ronnie Mac Keith

MARTHA

In the biblical story Martha was the sister of Lazarus and Mary Magdalene. Some author-ities believe that the Last Supper was held in Martha's house and that she served the meal. Eastern Orthodox tradition states that the siblings settled and died in Cyprus. Other authorities believe that they settled in the Pyrenees. It is not known why the name was chosen. **(1725 – 2007)**

Painting of Madonna and Child, by Jason Brooks 2005

MARY

It is not known after which Mary the ward was named but it was probably the Virgin Mary, mother of Jesus. **(1830s – 1997)**

MASSIE

See Grant Massie.

MAURICE CRAIG

Maurice Craig (1866 – 1935) went to Cambridge and Guy's, and qualified in 1892. He was appointed resident medical officer at Bethlem Hospital for the insane and resigned to succeed George Savage at Guy's in 1903. He was renowned for his considerate attitude to patients. However Craig was unpopular with the suffragettes as his gentle but persuasive methods often broke the resistance of those on hunger strike. He was a popular lecturer and teacher, keeping a balance between the old and new therapies at a time of great change. Craig and George Savage were renowned for being physicians to Virginia Woolf. He received a knighthood in 1928. **(1944 – 2000)**

MIRIAM

Miriam was probably named after the biblical elder sister of Moses and Aaron. When Pharaoh ordered that all Hebrew boy babies should be killed, Miriam placed Moses in a basket, on the riverbank, where Pharaoh's daughter would see him. The princess adopted the infant and hired Miriam's mother as the "wet nurse". Moses was therefore brought up by his own mother. **(1830s – 1997)**

NAAMAN

According to the Bible story Naaman was a Syrian army leader who contracted leprosy. The prophet Elisha told Naaman to dip himself seven times in the River Jordan, which cured him. Elisha declined payment and Naaman joined Elisha's faith. The name reminded the sick poor to pray for health. **(1725 – 1999)**

NEW CHILDREN'S WARD

New Children's Ward was named after its patients. **(1923 – 1936)**

NUFFIELD HOUSE

See St Thomas' list. **(1933 – open in 2008)**

OBSERVATION

The name is included in an internal telephone directory but its location is unknown. **(1990s)**

PATIENCE

Patience is considered a virtue by many religions. The name remains popular today. **(1725 – open in 2008)**

PETER BISHOP

The ward Peter Bishop was named after Peter Maxwell Farrow Bishop (1904 – 1979). The son of a Yorkshire doctor he qualified at Guy's in 1929. He then studied gynaecological endocrinology and, in 1933, he was appointed lecturer in physiological chemistry. In 1936 he was appointed the first Guy's consultant in clinical endocrinology. He was in charge of the emergency medical services at Guy's during the Second World War, after which he began travelling world-wide as guest professor. Bishop was a clear, concise communicator and received many honours. His research led to the development of the contraceptive pill. In 1967, his retirement year, he was appointed Master of the Society of Apothecaries. **(1974 – 1990s)**

PETERSHAM

Petersham was the name of a "watch house" (guard house) next to the south west corner of Guy's House. It was bought with money from the William Hunt bequest. It may not be entirely coincidental that Hunt lived in the village of Petersham near Richmond-upon-Thames. **(1829 – late 1800s)**

PHILIP

Philip is mentioned in an 1853 Guy's Report. There is no record as to why the Governors chose this name. **(possibly 1830s – late 1800s)**

QUEEN

The ward was probably named after Alexandra (1844 – 1925) wife of King Edward VII. She had married the then Prince in 1863. She was Danish and popular both when Princess of Wales and when she was Queen. Edward died in 1910 and she was given the courtesy title of Queen Mother **(1901 – open in 2008)**

RICHARD BRIGHT

See Bright

ROBERT GILLESPIE

Robert Gillespie (1897 – 1945) was born in Glasgow and, while training in Edinburgh, became interested in the causes of fatigue. He was appointed a psychiatrist at Guy's, aged only 29, having already assisted in writing a textbook. Gillespie stressed the importance of caring for a patient's mental, as well as physical, wellbeing. He introduced child psychiatry as a specialty. Thanks to a donation given in tribute to his pioneering work, Gillespie was able to design and build the York Clinic. Sadly he was a victim of depression and took his own life. **(1944 – 1997)**

RONNIE MAC KEITH

The ward was named after Ronald Charles Mac Keith (1908 – 1977). He was a general practitioner's son and trained at St Mary's Paddington, qualifying in 1933. He served in the Royal Navy during the Second World War. In 1948 he was appointed Consultant Paediatrician at Guy's where he introduced daily visiting for parents. Mac Keith brought about important advances in the care of psychologically and physically disabled

children. His work was honoured internationally. Mac Keith was the author of many medical books on child health and welfare. He retired in 1973. **(1980s – 2005)**

ROTHSCHILD

The name was a tribute to the Rothschild family who, for over 150 years, had supported the Evelina Hospital for Sick Children and Guy's Hospital. (see Evelina list) **(1975 – 2005)**

RUSKIN

See John Ruskin

RUSSELL BROCK

Russell Claude Brock (1903 – 1980) entered Guy's medical school from Christ's Hospital School in 1920. In 1929 he went to study thoracic surgery techniques in St Louis, USA. In 1936 he was appointed as a surgeon at Guy's. After serving in the Second World War he returned to Guy's and soon became known as one of the greatest pioneers of mitral valve surgery. Brock was also involved at an early stage with surgery for congenital heart conditions. He was knighted in 1954. In 1956 he learned that the old operating theatre of St Thomas' had been discovered. Thanks to his enthusiasm and funding the theatre was restored and opened as a museum. He was President of the Royal College of Surgeons of England from 1963 until 1966 and was made a life peer in 1965. He retired in 1968 but continued with private practice and lecturing. He was an exchange visiting clinician with Johns Hopkins Hospital, Baltimore and received many other honours. A prolific author, he wrote a biography of Astley Cooper and was editor of the Guy's Hospital Gazette for 25 years. After he died, the Lord Brock Memorial Trust was established to support the Old Operating Theatre and Herb Garret Museum. **(1990s –2004)**

RUTH

In the Bible story Ruth showed loyalty to her mother-in-law and converted to the Jewish religion. Her descendant was King David from whom Jesus is said to have been descended. This name would have had symbolic meaning to the sick poor. **(1830s – 1974)**

SAMARITAN

The biblical parable of the Good Samaritan appears in the Gospel of St Luke. Its moral remains applicable today – help should be given to all in need regardless of creed or culture. **(1725 – open in 2008)**

SARAH

Sarah is believed to have been named after the biblical Sarah who was the wife of Abraham, matriarch and mother of Isaac. The story recounts that Sarah was old when God permitted her to conceive and have one son. It was unusual to introduce biblical ward names in the 20th century but Sarah is a symbolic example of the reward that can come from faith and love. **(1998 – open in 2008)**

SARAH SWIFT

Sarah Swift (1854 – 1937) was born and educated near Boston, Lincolnshire. She trained (practical only) from 1877 at Dundee Royal Infirmary and worked in Dundee and Liverpool prior to moving to London in 1886/7. She visited the USA and Turkey and in 1890 entered Guy's as a paying probationer. The following year she was appointed Deputy Matron. She was Matron from 1900 until 1909. Miss Swift was small in stature but hugely impressive.

She was founder of the College of Nursing which opened in 1916 and became by 1921 the Royal College of Nursing (RCN). This ensured the future of nursing as a regulated and registered profession.

Miss Swift was variously President, Treasurer and Vice-President of the RCN and Matron in Chief of the Royal Naval Service, the British Red Cross Society and the Order of St John of Jerusalem in England. She was made a Dame of the British Empire and received other awards in recognition of her achievements. **(1946 – 1962)**

SAVAGE

See George Savage

SNOWSFIELDS

Snowsfields has been on maps of Southwark for centuries and probably referred originally to an area of land owned by a family named Snow. Snowsfields is the road that forms the southern boundary of Guy's. **(early 2000s – open in 2008)**

SPARE

The name is listed in the Governor' Reports as temporary accommodation. **(1852)**

STANLEY

See St Thomas' list. **(2004 – 2006)**

STARLING

Ernest Starling (1866 – 1927) entered Guy's Medical School in 1882. An outstanding student, he became a competent demonstrator and lecturer. His primary interest was physiology and in 1892 he published "The Elements of Human Physiology" subsequently moving to University College Hospital. In 1914 he returned to Guy's to take a refresher course enabling him to practise as a physician during the First World War. He worked in a military hospital and was advisor to the Government on dietetics. In 1927, Guy's celebrated the centenary of Bright's famous Reports on Medical Cases and intended to give one of five commemorative medals to Starling but he died suddenly before it could be presented. **(1974 – 1997)**

STEPHEN

Stephen is mentioned in the Court of Committees Reports of 16 March 1853 as being open. There is no record as to why the Governors chose the name. **(possibly 1830s – 1997)**

SWIFT

See Sarah Swift

SYMONDS

See Charles Symonds

TALBOT (see also Tabard Annex)

A Talbot was a large hound of a now extinct breed. A Court of Committees Report dated 4 December 1850 said: "it is resolved that The Talbot Inn be purchased and converted". Talbot ward was then listed in the Guy's Reports as temporary accommodation. **(1850 – 1853)**

TIMBO

Tim (Timbo) Ward was diagnosed with kidney problems in 1966 at the age of 13. He died when a renal transplant failed. At the time this type of surgery was in its infancy. In 1975 his mother, Elizabeth Ward, founded the Guy's Kidney Patient Association. When Bostock moved in the early 1990s and a new dialysis unit was being designed, Elizabeth Ward funded the specially designed children's treatment area which was named Timbo. **(1990s – 2005)**

VICTORIA

See Queen and see St Thomas' list.
It appears that usage sometimes varied
between Victoria and Queen Victoria.
(1938 – circa 2000)

WESTON

Weston was named after the eastern
boundary road of Guy's. At the turn of the
18th to 19th centuries, the Webb Weston
family owned the area named "Manor of the
Maze". Weston Street was named after the
family. **(1999 – 2005)**

WILKS

Samuel Wilks (1824 – 1912) was born in
Camberwell. On leaving school he attended
lectures at Guy's but enrolled at London
University to study medicine, qualifying in
1850. Wilks was a morbid anatomist at a time
when post-mortems became obligatory. He
was appointed as a physician in 1856 and
revived research at Guy's. He resigned from
Guy's in 1885 when appointed physician to
Queen Victoria. In 1892 Wilks was co-author,
with the historian G T Bettany, of the

"Biographical History of Guy's Hospital". Wilks
was made a Baronet in 1897.
(after 1936 – 1997)

WILLIAM GULL

William Withey Gull (1816 – 1890) was a poor
boy who was befriended by the Guy's
Treasurer, Benjamin Harrison, who housed
and educated him in London. Gull trained at
Guy's and his benefactor was able to secure
Gull junior positions. He was appointed
physician in 1851 and soon built a large
private practice. However, he continued
teaching at Guy's and wrote reports on
myxoedema and anorexia nervosa. Gull

William Gull

resigned in 1866 and in 1872 was made a Baronet.
(1950s – 1997)

WILLIAM LITTLE

William John Little (1810 – 1894) was born with a deformed foot and had polio as a child. Apprenticed first to an apothecary, he entered the London Hospital Medical School aged 18. In 1832 he was admitted to the Royal College of Surgeons of England. He travelled to Germany to study surgical techniques and then had corrective surgery on his foot. Little became an expert on deformities and founded the Royal National Orthopaedic Hospital in London. He did research on the link between neurological and orthopaedic conditions and described cerebral spastic palsy, now named Little's Disease.
(1974 – 1980s)

YORK CLINIC

York Clinic was funded by an anonymous donor and built on land paid for by Lord Nuffield. The reason for the choice of name is unknown. The donor wished to honour Guy's psychiatrist Robert Gillespie by providing inpatient care for emotionally disturbed patients of limited means.
(1944 – open in 2008)

EVELINA CHILDREN'S HOSPITAL

The Evelina Hospital for Sick Children was founded at a time of increasing public concern at the high rate of sickness and death of children. In the mid-19th century, illness was often caused by poor diet and sanitation. Contaminated water and dark, damp, over-crowded slums aggravated the problems. However, it was one tragic event that led to the foundation of a children's hospital in Southwark.

Evelina was the wife of Baron Ferdinand de Rothschild. In 1864, a year before her marriage, she was involved in a railway accident. It is not known why this event became connected with her death two years later when she went into premature labour leading to the birth of a stillborn son. As a memorial to his wife, the Baron decided to fund a lying-in (maternity) hospital. However, Dr Arthur Farre, an obstetrician and family friend, who had attended the confinement and death of Evelina, suggested that there was a greater need for a children's hospital. Southwark was chosen because, as a child, Evelina had accompanied her mother on visits to the slums in the area. Dr Farre advised the architect, Marsh Nelson, on the planning of the hospital and the first patients were admitted to the "Evelina Hospital for Sick Children" in 1869.

The Baron financed the building of the Evelina and met the expenses of its first 30 beds for the first two years. He was President of its Management Committee and gave generous financial, and advisory, support until his death in 1898.

The Hospital was built on an almost rectangular site known as South Sea Court. It was bounded on one long side by Lombard Street and on the other by the curve of Southwark Bridge Road. The Hospital had four storeys

with its entrance on Quilp Street. The outpatients wing had its own entrance.

Parents were not charged and initially only 30 of the planned 100 cots could be staffed. Although it is almost certain that the wards were named from the outset, they are seldom mentioned in the Records.

The basement housed the main kitchens, a separate kosher kitchen, a washhouse and support services. On the ground floor were the Lady Superintendent's office, the Board Room and the Ladies' Committee office.

On the first and second floors were identical long wards with the windows overlooking Southwark Bridge Road. The access corridor also had windows which ensured excellent light and ventilation in accordance with

1 Front entrance of the Evelina Hospital for Sick Children
2 Wall plaque installed in 2004 on the site of the original hospital
3 Nurse and child c. 1900

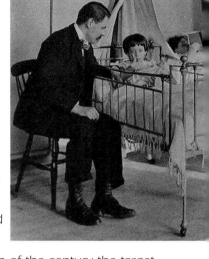

Florence Nightingale's principles. There was a playroom, toilet facilities and four fireplaces. These allowed staff to divide the ward if required. Also, on each floor were three small wards: one for Jewish children, one for cases of whooping cough and one for infants.

On the third (attic) floor were bedrooms for the nurses and other staff, and a quarantine ward for "doubtful cases". In addition there were two isolation wards above the outpatients department.

In its first year, over 300 children were admitted.

In 1871, The Times enthused "The wards of the Evelina are the only places in which the children of the London poor can be seen undisguised by dirt; and here cleanliness whether personal or domestic obviously reigns supreme".

There was an urgent need to open more cots. Due to fund-raising appeals the number of cots had doubled by 1880 but even at the turn of the century the target of 100 cots had not been achieved. In 1903 there were still only 68 general, four diphtheria, and four isolation cots available.

From the outset it was realised that there was nothing to be gained by sending children back to filth and misery immediately on discharge. In 1874 convalescence was introduced and a fund to support it established. In 1928, an anonymous donor enabled a purpose-built convalescent home to be built near Henley-on-Thames.

In 1892 the Evelina became a publicly-funded institution. By the time the Baron died, in 1898, the Evelina was providing an outstanding service for the sick poor children of London.

DEVELOPMENT IN THE 20th CENTURY

Between 1900 and 1914 the Evelina continued to expand its services. The funding to make this possible ranged from large donations, such as that from the Estate of Siegfried Rudolph Zunz, to small contributions from individuals. In 1903, the attic accommodation was improved by the construction of a mansard-roof. At this time lifts were installed and the quarantine ward was refurbished to form another isolation ward. Staff numbers were adequate and the unacceptably high 20% mortality recorded in 1908 gradually fell due to advances in medical and nursing techniques. In addition to Farre, many eminent physicians and surgeons were associated with the Evelina's development.

All changed with the onset of the First World War in 1914, when both staff and funds were redirected. However, a successful campaign was launched in which 'The public are...confidently asked to help this Institution...for children... whose lives are of vital importance to the Nation".

3

1 Evelina 1895
2 Doctor on his rounds, early 20th century
3 Nurse and baby, early 20th century

One cot was funded in memory of Nurse Edith Cavell (1865 – 1915) who was executed in Belgium for helping allied soldiers to escape. From 1918 parents were asked to make a contribution whenever possible and continual fundraising appeals were necessary to keep the Hospital functioning.

In 1937 plans for a comprehensive refurbishment were drawn up. The work was due to start in 1939, but the outbreak of the Second World War halted this project. In August 1939, the inpatients were evacuated and the Evelina became a first-aid post with children being treated only as outpatients. Two wards were open for a few months in 1940 but were closed when, in November, a direct hit demolished **Lionel**, the kitchens and outpatients area. The hospital was patched up and remained open until the V2 attacks in 1944. There was further blast damage but no more direct hits. In 1945 the hospital was again repaired and reopened. There were no casualties among patients or staff while in the Evelina during the war.

Following the end of the war in 1945, the Evelina struggled to stay open whilst its future was debated. In 1947 it merged with the Children's Department of nearby Guy's Hospital which ensured the Evelina children had access to a wide range of services and staff. The Evelina could also play a role in the training of doctors, nurses and other hospital students.

In 1863 Florence Nightingale had proposed that all children in hospital should receive education. In 1949 the Guy's Evelina Hospital school was opened – the first in an acute hospital in the UK.

In 1952 Aural, one of the original fever wards on the first floor, was converted into an infant's unit and renamed **Baron Ferdinand de Rothschild** ward. There were six cots in small cubicles and a seventh cubicle with a bed for the mother. This specialist unit treated babies with congenital heart defects.

In the early 1960s, children with psychiatric problems were admitted into **Hector Cameron**, a specially designed seven-bedded unit.

As an indication of improved health and conditions generally, in 1962 routine convalescence ceased.

The ward names at the Hospital during its final 20 years are known. On the first floor were **Evelina**, **Hector Cameron**, **Charlotte**, **Ferdinand Rothschild**, **Lionel** and **Mayer Amschel** (all medical). The surgical wards on the second floor were **Annie Zunz** (general) and **Helen Lucas** (orthopaedic). The operating theatres were on the floor above.

In the early 1970s, it was decided to move all children's services into Guy's Hospital. The Evelina was closed and, in 1976, demolished. The site is now Mint Street Park, a public garden. Part of the north-west outer wall of the Evelina was retained and in 2004 a commemorative plaque was fixed to the old bricks. The words are engraved and in "low relief" are the busts of Baroness Evelina de Rothschild, Alice Cross, Lady Superintendent from 1879 until 1903, Baron Ferdinand de Rothschild and Dr Arthur Farre.

EVELINA AT GUY'S 1976 – 2005

The paediatric unit moved into purpose-built accommodation on the ninth to twelfth floors of the newly-built Guy's Tower in 1976. There were eight wards with about 100 beds or cots in total. The unit was named the Evelina Children's Hospital.

On the ninth floor **Caleb** and **Diplock** were a six-bedded burns unit and a 17-bedded isolation ward. **Dickens** was an 18-bedded renal and general ward.

On the tenth floor, **William Little** (later renamed **Ronnie Mac Keith**) was a 21-bedded medical ward with three additional beds for metabolic conditions and **Hector Cameron** was a 10-bedded psychiatric ward.

On the next floor, **Rothschild** was a 22-bedded cardiac-surgery ward and **The Borough** a ward for children needing intensive post-operative care.

Arthur Farre, on the twelfth floor, housed the special care baby unit with a three-bedded flat for parents.

It was apparent that, as many parents lived at a distance, accommodation close to Guy's was needed.

The Evelina Family Trust Charity was formed to raise funds. In 1990, Ronald McDonald House opened in Weston Street, with 18 rooms for the families of sick children receiving treatment in the Evelina. It was the first such hotel in the UK and is open today.

Following the creation of the Guy's and St Thomas' NHS Foundation Trust in 1993, the need for a purpose-built hospital for children was recognised. The **Riddell House** site at St Thomas' was identified as suitable.

EVELINA IN LAMBETH 2005 – TODAY

Late in 1999, Sir Michael Hopkins won the competition to be the architect of the new Evelina. His design was greatly influenced by Florence Nightingale's concept of large windows for natural light. The building costs, in excess of £50 million, were mostly met by the Guy's and St Thomas' Charity – the largest single donation ever made to the NHS. A further £10 million for state of the art equipment was raised by the Evelina Hospital Appeal.

1 Evelina Children's Hospital © Paul Tyagi for Hopkins Architects Ltd
2 Tree of Life © Richard Bailey
3 Children of the World © Richard Bailey
4 Floor symbols © Hopkins Architects Ltd

The foundation stone was laid in 2003 and the Evelina Children's Hospital opened to patients on 31 October 2005.

Uniquely, young patients were consulted and their ideas were incorporated into the design of the new hospital. From the viewpoint of this book, the greatest impact of this was the children's renaming of wards. They chose the natural world using colour-coded signs and pictures. This system helps the very young and those speaking any one of the 140 different languages used in Lambeth alone, to easily find their way.

Art works are a feature on the St Thomas' site. Before Riddell House was demolished a tree had been created by Thomas Kilpper. Made from old floor boards and furniture, its roots were in the basement swimming pool and its branches spread up to the roof. Two new works have been placed outside the Evelina. One is "The Tree of Life" by Chris Plowman, and the

other, five figures depicting "Children of the World", the work of Frederick Landowsky. Striking features of the building itself are the arching glass roof, the terracotta exterior, and the brilliant colours used for decorating the interior.

There is plant in the basement. The ground floor reception and outpatient level is named Ocean, with Sun and Moon the two red "rocket" lifts at each end. A helter-skelter designed by Lillian Lijn is in the play area. Pictures of various sea creatures indicate the clinics, toilets and other services at this level.

Arctic is the first floor. Each outpatient unit has a name and pictures, including a Snowy Owl for children with peanut allergies. The counselling room was funded by the family of Edward Mansell. In 1947, he was the second UK child to receive,

4

1

1 Evelina at night © Paul Tyagi for Hopkins Architects Ltd
2 Andrew with one of the Chipolatas performing on Beach.

at Guy's, the life-saving Blalock-Taussig operation for the "blue baby" heart condition known as Fallot's Tetralogy.

Forest, the second floor, is home to the operating theatres, the eight-bedded recovery area and the 20-bedded intensive care unit.

The wards are on the next three floors occupying half the width of the building.

Each ward has a welcoming play area adjacent to the entry door, a few single rooms, seminar room and, uniquely, beside each bed or cot a drop-down bed so that a parent can stay if required.

On Beach, the third floor, are the school, café and space for performing arts. The ward areas are **Seahorse**, **Turtle** and **Crab**. The 31 beds are for renal, neurology and some minor surgery patients.

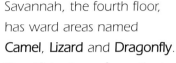

Savannah, the fourth floor, has ward areas named **Camel**, **Lizard** and **Dragonfly**. The 42 beds are for patients with cardiac, metabolic and other medical conditions.

Mountain, the fifth floor, has ward areas named **Bird**, **Bear** and **Deer**. The 42 beds are mainly for surgical patients.

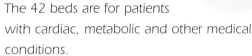

The top floor, Sky, is the administration centre for the Hospital.

THE FUTURE

The needs of the local population have altered but the Evelina remains as essential today as on the day opened. Long may it continue to serve young patients and their parents.

THE WARDS OF EVELINA CHILDREN'S HOSPITAL

Dates at the end of an entry indicate when the ward name was possibly first used and when the name was last used.

ANNIE ZUNZ

Annie Sophia Zunz (1845 – 1896) was the wife of Seigfried Rudolph Zunz, a German metal merchant, who lived in Wimbledon. She predeceased her husband. He died in 1899 leaving much of his considerable fortune in the Annie Zunz Bequest for distribution to hospitals. He specified that wards were to be named Annie Zunz. Many London hospitals benefited, including the Evelina.
(after 1899 – 1975)

ARTHUR FARRE

See Guy's list.

AURAL

Although the word is generally associated with the ear it is probable that the ward was named for another meaning. The word "aura" can be used to describe the sensations which precede an attack of an ailment such as epilepsy or hysteria. Aural was opened as a fever ward making its name appropriate. **(possibly 1869 – 1952)**

BARON FERDINAND DE ROTHSCHILD

See Ferdinand Rothschild

BOROUGH

See Guy's list

CALEB

See Guy's list

CHARLOTTE

Charlotte was the first name of the mothers of both Evelina and Ferdinand de Rothschild.

CHARLOTTE DE ROTHSCHILD

Charlotte de Rothschild (1807 – 1859) was born in England, the eldest child of Hannah and Nathan de Rothschild, who was the third of Mayer Amschel's five sons. In 1826 she married her Viennese cousin, Anselm von Rothschild. Ferdinand was their sixth child. He took the name de Rothschild after her death.

CHARLOTTE VON ROTHSCHILD

Charlotte von Rothschild (1819 – 1884) was born in Naples, Italy, the daughter of Carl Mayer von Rothschild, the fourth of Mayer Amschel's five sons. Her mother was Adelheid Hertz. In 1836, Charlotte married her cousin, Lionel de Rothschild. The couple had three sons and two daughters, the younger being Evelina. Charlotte took her daughters on philanthropic visits to the poor and is known to have visited The Borough. It is almost certain that the ward was named after her. She and Ferdinand personally funded the Evelina for its first two years. She visited regularly and was a member of the Ladies' Committee. **(possibly 1869 – 1975)**

DICKENS

See Guy's list

DIPLOCK

See Guy's list

EVELINA

The Evelina was named after Baroness Evelina de Rothschild (1839 – 1866). She was the second child of Lionel and Charlotte de Rothschild. Evelina married Baron Ferdinand de Rothschild in July 1865. Tragically, in December 1866, Evelina died in premature childbirth and her son was stillborn. The devastated Baron intended building a maternity hospital in her memory. Arthur Farre persuaded him to build a hospital for poor children near the slums of the Borough. **(possibly 1869 – 1976)**

FARRE

see Arthur Farre Guy's list

1 Baroness Evelina de Rothschild
2 Charlotte de Rothschild (née Charlotte von Rothschild), mother of Evelina
Reproduced with the permission of The Rothschild Archive

FERDINAND ROTHSCHILD

Ferdinand Rothschild was named after Baron Ferdinand James Anselm de Rothschild (1839 – 1898). He was the sixth child of Charlotte Mayer and Anselm von Rothschild. Although born in Paris, Ferdinand spent his youth in Frankfurt before moving to Vienna where his father's banking business was based.

Ferdinand stayed in Vienna until 1860, when he moved to London. He altered his name from "von" to "de" Rothschild. In July 1865 Ferdinand married his cousin Evelina de Rothschild. It was as a result of her death in premature childbirth in December 1866 that the Evelina Hospital for Sick Children was built. It was a lasting memorial to her from a husband devastated by her early death. Baron Ferdinand financed the building, whilst he and Evelina's mother Charlotte paid for all the running costs of the first two years. Their interest in the Hospital was lifelong. Baron de Rothschild was a High Sheriff of Buckinghamshire, and in 1883 was elected Liberal MP for Aylesbury. Waddesdon Manor the mansion he built between 1874 and 1889, was in his constituency. **(possibly 1869 – 1975)**

HECTOR CAMERON

See Guy's list. **(circa 1960 – 2005)**

HELEN LUCAS

Helen Lucas (1835 – 1918) was a close friend of the Rothschild family. Helen Goldsmid was the eldest of nine children and well educated by her parents. She married a merchant, Lionel Lucas, in 1855 and the couple had two children before his early death in 1862. As a wealthy widow, she was a generous philanthropist. She was totally committed to family life and discouraged the use of day nurseries and youth clubs. She worked to improve welfare and education for the poor of all

Ferdinand Rothschild
Reproduced with the permission of The Rothschild Archive

faiths. She taught both the language and culture of Judaism. **(possibly 1869 – 1975)**

ISOLATION

Self explanatory. **(1869 – mid-20th century)**

LIONEL

Lionel de Rothschild (1808 – 1875) was the son of Nathan Mayer Rothschild (Mayer Amschel's son in London) and Hannah Barent Cohen. Lionel married his cousin Charlotte von Rothschild, daughter of Carl (Mayer Amschel's son in Naples). The couple had two daughters and three sons. Their younger daughter was Evelina. Their eldest son, Nathan would, in 1885, become the first Jewish member of the House of Lords. Lionel was elected to the City of London parliamentary seat in 1847 and was returned another four times – in 1849, 1852 and, twice in 1857. Being Jewish, he was not able to take his seat until 1858 when MPs were no longer required to swear an oath on the New Testament. He was an MP until 1874 and a lifelong benefactor of the Evelina Hospital for Sick Children. **(possibly 1869 – 1975)**

MAYER AMSCHEL

Mayer Amschel Rothschild (1744 – 1812) was born in Frankfurt-am-Main. The family's success was said to have been promoted when Mayer Amschel helped manage the finances of the immensely wealthy exiled Wilhelm IX, Landgrave of Hesse-Cassel, when Napoleon was trying to conquer Europe. In 1770, Mayer Amschel married Gutle Schnapper. The couple's five sons opened Rothschild branches in Vienna (Salomon Mayer), London (Nathan Mayer), Naples (Carl Mayer) and Paris (James [Jacob] Mayer) whilst the eldest, Amschel Mayer, stayed in Frankfurt. Mayer Amschel was the great-grandfather of Baron Ferdinand. **(possibly 1869 – 1975)**

The Elector of Hesse entrusting Mayer Amschel with his treasure, watercolour by J Oppenheimer
Reproduced with the permission of The Rothschild Archive

RONNIE MAC KEITH

See Guy's list

ROTHSCHILD

Rothschild is German for red shield which was the house sign of the family home in Frankfurt in the early 18th century. When, later in that century, Mayer Amschel Bauer opened the general trader family business which grew into the banking empire, he adopted the name Rothschild although the family home at the time was named Green Shield. The ward name was possibly chosen to represent all the family members who had been philanthropists over two centuries. **(1975 – 2005)**

WILLIAM JOHN LITTLE

See Guy's list

ZUNZ

See Annie Zunz

Evelina Children's Hospital atrium, from Beach
© Paul Tyagi for Hopkins Architects Ltd

DERIVATIONS OF OTHER NAMES

Although the following are not ward names they are interesting in the context of the Hospitals' histories

BERMONDSEY WING (GUY'S)

Bermondsey is derived from the name of a Viking called Bjornmond or Bermond, who settled on an island (ey or eyot) in the Thames. This became known as Bermond's Eyot.

(new in 2008)

DREADNOUGHT (ST THOMAS')

The first Seamen's Hospital opened in 1821 on the Grampus, a ship moored near Greenwich. Dreadnought replaced the Grampus in 1831. In 1872 Dreadnought came on land into the Naval Pensioners Infirmary at Greenwich. For the next 114 years, the Hospital treated merchant seafarers, minimising the time patients spent away from their ships. By the 1980s demand for the service had fallen and the Hospital's Georgian building was prohibitively expensive to maintain. In 1986, its administrators, one ophthalmic surgeon and Northumberland and Somerset wards moved into St Thomas'. The Dreadnought Office remains open to merchant seafarers.

(1986 – open in 2008)

GASSIOT (ST THOMAS')

Charles Gassiot (1826 – 1902) was a wine merchant in the City of London and, for 30 years, a Governor of St Thomas'. He bequeathed money to build a nurses' home which also houses St Thomas' Home for paying patients. The original Gassiot House was badly damaged in the Second World War but was in use until the late 1960s when it was demolished. The new Gassiot House was opened in 1972. Today it accommodates Simon Hotel, executive offices for The Trust, the Nightingale Fellowship and other facilities.

(1906 – open in 2008)

GORDON MUSEUM (GUY'S)

The Gordon Museum was named after Robert Gordon who was born in 1829 in Dumfries. Aged 17 he entered a law office in Liverpool but in 1849 moved to New York. He

prospered, returning to London in 1884 where he joined J S Morgan & Co. He was appointed a Guy's Hospital Governor in 1898 and became a generous benefactor. His first recorded gift was in 1900 when he endowed a lectureship and laboratory for experimental pathology. Eight years later he funded new equipment for the department. His major donation was in 1904 when he paid for the entire cost of the ornate, galleried Museum. **(1904 – open in 2008)**

HARRISON (GUY'S)

Benjamin Harrison (1771 – 1856) was the powerful Treasurer of Guy's from 1797 until 1848. He was secretary to the medical school, appointee of senior medical staff and renowned for his varied administrative skills. He brought about numerous important developments during his term of office. He kept meticulous records, always took action for the good of Guy's and likened opposition to his ideas for progress as rebellion.

HENRIETTA RAPHAEL NURSES' HOME (GUY'S)

Henrietta Raphael was the wife of Henry Lewis Raphael (1832 – 1899) a member of a philanthropic family of stock brokers and bankers. Henrietta died in 1897 and her husband donated £20,000 in her memory which the Governors used to finance a much-needed nurses home. He died before its 1901 opening. The inclusion of a swimming pool was made possible by donations from Walter Raphael and Henry's son Herbert. Other family members, Ernest and Cecil Raphael, donated £2,000 to create a Fund, the interest being used to assist nurses in need. The building is now part of the University and is no longer a nurses' home. **(open in 2008)**

1 Robert Gordon
2 Swimming pool in Henrietta Raphael Nurses' Home

HODGKIN BUILDING (GUY'S)

The Hodgkin Building was named after Dr Thomas Hodgkin (1798 – 1866) who qualified

1

in 1823 at Guy's. He travelled in France and Italy but returned to Guy's and helped to form the Guy's School of Medicine. His interest in pathology led to his appointment as museum curator and demonstrator of morbid anatomy. He was a prolific writer and was the first to describe enlargement of the lymph glands and spleen now named Hodgkin's Disease.

Hodgkin founded the Ethnological Society and developed an interest in the study of philology. He frequently travelled in Europe and the Middle East with his friend Sir Moses Montefiore. It was in Jaffa, in 1866, that Hodgkin died of dysentery. Montefiore had an inscribed granite obelisk erected there in memory of an extraordinary man. **(open in 2008)**

HUNT'S HOUSE (GUY'S)

Sir William Hunt lived in Petersham and died in 1828. As a result of his huge bequest Hunt's House was built and well endowed. In 1997 the building was demolished.

2

JERICHO (ST THOMAS')

Jericho can be used humorously as being a remote place to which one is consigned. The name for this night nurses accommodation was therefore apt as it was located between Blocks 7 and 8. After bomb damage in the Second World War Jericho was converted to become the South Wing Operating Theatre. In 1977 the Renal Unit moved into Jericho and the name was no longer used. **(1930s – 1977)**

KEATS HOUSE (GUY'S)

Keats House is in St Thomas Street. The 18th century house is named after the famous poet John Keats (see Guy's list). In 1946 the house was converted for private consultations and is open today.

McNAIR ANTENATAL OUTPATIENTS DEPARTMENT (GUY'S)

Arthur James McNair (1887 – 1964) qualified at Guy's in 1911, and worked as a surgical officer during the First World War. In 1925, he returned to Guy's having been appointed to the obstetric and gynaecological staff. He was renowned for his skill, liked by patients, respected by students and held in high esteem by colleagues. McNair was a foundation member of the Royal College of Obstetricians and Gynaecologists of which he was Vice-President from 1952 to 1955. He retired in 1952 and was appointed honorary consultant to St Thomas'.
(1974 - open in 2008)

NEW HUNT'S HOUSE (GUY'S)

New Hunt's House was built on the site of the original Hunt's House and was opened in 1999. It houses the Information Centre and teaching and research facilities for King's College London, Guy's campus.
(1999 – open in 2008)

NUFFIELD HOUSE (GUY'S)

Lord Nuffield (see St Thomas' list) was a philanthropist who gave generously to both St Thomas' and Guy's. In 1935 Nuffield House was opened at Guy's as a private hospital. It remained open throughout the Second World War. **(1935 – open in 2008)**

3

RIDDELL HOUSE (ST THOMAS')

Riddell House was named after Lady Annie Riddell who, in 1934, gave £100,000 to build a nurses' home and rooms for the Preliminary Training School. It was opened in 1937. Lady Riddell also donated a collection of Florence Nightingale's artefacts. These included bricks from the South Street home, antique furniture and works of art. She was herself a "Nightingale" nurse and her late husband had, in the 1920s, partly funded St Thomas' House. Riddell House was badly damaged during the Second World War. It was demolished to create space for the new Evelina Children's Hospital.

(1937 – demolished in 2002)

ST THOMAS' HOUSE (ST THOMAS')

St Thomas' House was built as a residential club for medical students. It was opened in 1927 as a memorial to those who died in the First World War. Lord Riddell, a Governor, gave a large donation towards the building costs. After academic changes in 1998 the building was used for various offices. In 2008 the St Thomas' Campus Medical School Library moved in. **(1927 – open in 2008)**

SHARPINGTON STAFF CLUB (ST THOMAS')

The Club is named after Robert Sharpington. Mike Messer, former staff photographer to St Thomas', wrote "I remember Mr Sharpington. Robert, Bob to close friends, was St Thomas' public relations officer. He was, I thought, always very correct, like an RAF officer. When he rang our department he always observed the correct order of seniority. He would ask for Mr Pache, then Mr Gregory and failing that he asked for me! We were Medical School staff and not meant to take pictures for Hospital staff". **(1971 – open in 2008)**

SHEPHERD (ST THOMAS' AND GUY'S)

William Shepherd and his son Sir Percy were both Governors and benefactors.

SHEPHERD HALL (ST THOMAS')

Sir Percy supplied the funds to build the William Shepherd Memorial Hall known as Shepherd Hall. It was built in 1924, as a nurses' dining room. It is in use today as a staff dining roof and as a venue for receptions and meetings. **(1924 – open in 2008)**

SHEPHERD'S HOUSE (GUY'S)

In 1917, accommodation was needed for various services including the Massage and Remedial Exercise School which had opened in 1913. More residential accommodation for nurses was also needed. The rebuilding programme incurred a large debt which Sir Percy Shepherd covered. Shepherd's House is named after his father. Today the building is part of King's College London, Guy's campus. **(1921 – open in 2008)**

SOUTHWARK WING (GUY'S)

The word Southwark is derived from Anglo-Saxon. The people of "Suthringa" which became "Sudwerca" and then South, worked hard "Geweorche" to build a "burgh" (a defensive fortification). Guy's is in the London borough of Southwark. **(new in 2008)**

TABARD ANNEX (GUY'S)

Tabard Annex is the name of the building housing Guy's Oncology Unit. It is known that

The Tabard Inn was open in 1306 on what is now Borough High Street. A tabard was a long coat and then was used for a knight's sleeveless tunic. In Chaucer's Canterbury Tales, written in the 1380s, the host owns The Tabard Inn. The Tabard was destroyed by fire in 1676. It was rebuilt and renamed The Talbot. When in the 1870s the Talbot Inn was demolished to create space for the boiler room and Works Department, the building was given the name Tabard House. It was badly damaged in the Second World War. Tabard House is used today by the Guy's Hospital works department. **(new in 2008)**

The Tabard or Talbot Inn

SOURCES

BOOKS

Boast M. *The Story of The Borough* London: London Borough of Southwark, 1997

Cameron HC. *Mr Guy's Hospital 1726 – 1948* London: Longmans, Green and Co, 1954

Cockett F and D (eds.) *The War Diary of St Thomas's Hospital 1939 – 1945* Newport, Gwent: The Starling Press Ltd, 1991

Cowles V. *The Rothschilds A family of fortune* London: Weidenfield and Nicholson, 1973 Revised 1979

Everyman's Encyclopedia fifth edition London: Readers Union J M Dent and Sons, 1968

Golding B. *An Historical Account of St Thomas's Hospital* London: Printed for Longman Hurst, Rees Orme & Browne, 1819

Graves C. *The Story of St Thomas's 1106 – 1947* London: Distributed by Faber and Faber for St Thomas's Hospital, 1947

Handler CE (ed.) *Guy's Hospital 250 Years* London: Guy's Hospital Gazette, 1976

McInnes EM. *St Thomas' Hospital* London: Special Trustees for St Thomas' Hospital, 2nd enlarged edition 1990

Parsons FG. *The History of St Thomas's Hospital Vol. I II III.* London: Methuen & Co, 1932, 1934 and 1936

Parsons FG. *Scenes from the life of St Thomas's Hospital 1106 to the present time.* London: 1938

Priestley H. *The Evelina: the story of a London Children's Hospital 1869 – 1969* London: Evelina Hospital Committee of Management

Rhodes P. Dr John Leake's Hospital. *The History of the new (New Westminster) General Lying-in Hospital, York Road, Lambeth 1765 – 1971* London: Davis-Poynter, 1977

Ripman HA (ed.) *Guy's Hospital 1725 – 1948*
London: Guy's Hospital Gazette Committee,
1951
Wake R. *The Nightingale Training School
1860 – 1996* London: Haggerston Press,
1998

Wilks S and Bettany GT. *A Biographical History
of Guy's Hospital* London: Ward, Lock,
Bowden and Co, 1892

PERIODICALS

Guy's Hospital Gazette – various articles

Nightingale Fellowship Journal Jubilee Edition
1935; Vol. 5 various articles

St Thomas's Hospital Gazette
various articles

ARTICLES

Buck K. *The St Christopher Fund Story*
The Old Lady (Bank of England Staff
Publication) 1961 June Vol.37 80-82

Joseph M and Joseph P. *History of the Evelina
Children's Hospital.*
GKT Gazette 2002 January Vol.115
No. 2506: 44-47

Knight RK. *Lots in a Name* Guy's Hospital
Gazette 1997; Vol. 110 No. 2467

McInnes EM. *Wards have names* St Thomas's
Hospital Gazette 1955; Vol. 53 No. 5: 192-
195

WEBSITES

Oxford Dictionary of National Biography
Online: http://www.oxforddnb.com
(accessed 6 June 2008)

MUSEUMS AND ARCHIVES

Florence Nightingale Museum, Gassiot House,
2 Lambeth Palace Road, London SE1 7EW
www.florence-nightingale.co.uk

Gordon Museum, Hodgkin House, Guy's
Hospital Campus, London SE1 9RT

www.kcl.ac.uk/teares/gktvc/vc/gordon/index.
html
London Metropolitan Archives, Northampton
Road, London EC1R OHB
www.cityoflondon.gov.uk/Corporation/leisure
_heritage/libraries_archives_museums_galleries
/lma/lma.htm

Southwark Local History Library, 211 Borough
High Street, London SE1 1JA
www.southwark.gov.uk/Uploads/FILE_6308.p
df

OTHER MATERIAL

The Chartulary of St Thomas's Hospital – 13th
14th and 15th Century records now part of
the Stowe Manuscript in the British Museum
(referred to by Parsons)

Guy's Annual Reports

St Thomas' Hospital Treasurer's Annual Reports

Reports of the Grand Committee of the
Governors of St Thomas' Hospital since the
16th Century, held at the London
Metropolitan Archives
A Return to Health (Guidelines for
Rehabilitating the South Wing) Donald W
Insall and Associates December 1979

New Guy's House
1960s commissioning booklet

Guy's Tower
1970s commissioning booklet

Philip Harris House (Thomas Guy House) 1990
Contract Commencement booklet and 1991
Topping Out Ceremony booklet

Evelina Children's Hospital 2005 Media Pack

ALPHABETICAL LIST OF WARDS

BY HOSPITAL

ST THOMAS' HOSPITAL

Abdiel
Abraham
Adamson
Adelaide
Alan Apley
Albert
Alexandra
Alfred
Alice
Anne
Arthur
Beatrice
Becket
Bowes
Braxton Hicks
Bristow
Charity
Cheselden
Christian
City of London
Clayton
Clinical
Cutts
Dorcas
Doulton

Edward (in Southwark)
Edward (in Lambeth)
Elizabeth
Evan Jones
Faith
Florence
Garland
George
George Perkins
Great Wards
Grosvenor
Gullan
Gynaecology
Haydon
Helen
Henry
Hillyers
Holden
Howard
Isaac
Jacob
Job
Jonah/Jonas
Judith
King's
Lane-Fox

Lansdell
Lazarus
Leopold
Lilian
Lloyd Still
Louise
Luke
Lydia
Magdalen
Makins
Mark
Mary
Mead
Mitchiner
Naple's or Naples
New
Nightingale
Nightlayers/Nightlodgers
Noah's Ark/Noah
Northumberland
Nuffield
Ophthalmic
Page
Queen's
Regency
Robert Willan

Royal Eye

St Thomas' Home

SANDS

Sarah Swift

Scutari

Seymour

Simon

Simon Hotel

Somerset

Stanley

Stephen

Susannah

Sweat

Thomas Bateman

Tobias

Victoria

Wardroper

Westminster Unit

William

William Gull

Wrigley

GUY'S HOSPITAL

Accident

Addison

Arthur Farre

Astley Cooper

Aston Key

Barnabas

Barnaby

Billet

Blundell

Borough

Bostock

Braxton Hicks

Bright

Brook

Caleb

Chapel

Charity

Charles Symonds

Christopher

Clinical

Cornelius

Cross

Dickens

Diplock

Dorcas

Esther

Evelina

Evelyn

Extra

Eye Infirmary

Florence

Frederick

George Savage

Grant Massie

Hector Cameron

Hedley Atkins

Hilton

Hurst

Job

John

John Dickson

John Ruskin

Keats

Lazarus

Lever

Luke

Lunatic House

Lydia

Martha

Mary

Maurice Craig

Miriam

Naaman

New Children's Ward

Nuffield House

Observation

Patience

Peter Bishop

Petersham

Philip

Queen

Robert Gillespie

Ronnie Mac Keith

Rothschild

Russell Brock

Ruth

Samaritan

Sarah

Sarah Swift

Snowsfields

Spare

Stanley

Starling

Stephen

Talbot

Timbo

Victoria

Weston

Wilks

William Gull

William Little

York Clinic

EVELINA HOSPITAL

Annie Zunz

Arthur Farre

Aural

Baron Ferdinand

Borough

Caleb

Charlotte de Rothschild

Charlotte von Rothschild

Dickens

Diplock

Evelina

Ferdinand Rothschild

Hector Cameron

Helen Lucas

Isolation

Lionel

Mayer Amschel

Ronnie Mac Keith

Rothschild

William Little

OTHER NAMES

Bermondsey Wing

Dreadnought

Gassiot

Gordon Museum

Harrison

Henrietta Raphael Nurses'

Home

Hodgkin Building

Hunt's House

Jericho

Keats House

McNair Antenatal

Outpatients Department

New Hunt's House

Nuffield House

Riddell House

St Thomas' House

Sharpington Staff Club

Shepherd

Shepherd Hall

Shepherd's House

Southwark Wing

Tabard Annex